THE ULTIMATE INTERACTIVE REVISION BOOK

NATIONAL 5
CHEMISTRY

written by:
Peter & Lesley Johnson

Published by
Kitchen Chemistry
23 Edderston Road
Peebles

ISBN 978-0-9934494-0-6

Images Credits:
The majority of images are taken from Wikimedia Commons. Every effort has been made to contact the copyright holder for images, if you identify your work and it has not been credited please contact Peter & Lesley Johnson (kitchenchemistry@tiscali.co.uk)

Acknowledgement:
The authors would like to thank Graeme Mitchell & Charlie Kerr of Stewart's Melville College for their support in developing the activities in this book. Also Fiona Neave of The Mary Erskine School and Alison Saxon for proof reading and feedback. Special thanks also to Howard and Gwen Johnson.

Note that answers to all the games, activities and practice questions can be found at the following website:

www.ultimate-revision-books.co.uk

Printed by Bell & Bain Ltd, Glasgow

Contents Page

How to make the most of this book

Lets face it……. revision can be boring!!!

Reading your notes or a textbook, copying facts and information out, then turning these into shorter notes may help you remember information but it can be slow, tedious and boring! More importantly it's not the most effective way of learning as you don't have to think much. Thinking is key to remembering information, the more you have to think about something the more you are going to remember it. **Active learning** is about getting you to look at and think about the information in lots of different ways; and then using that information in a variety of activities that are much more interesting than sitting looking at pages & pages of writing.

This book is split up into short topics, with a summary page of the key ideas at the start. You should look through this information and make sure you understand what it's about. If you don't understand it look back at your own notes or textbook; even better speak to your teacher and ask them to explain it to you. Once you understand the material it's time to learn it. To help you there are pages with different activities all linked to those key ideas. Keep flicking back to the summary page to check you are getting it right, as none of the activities are there to test you, they are all about getting you to use the correct information in lots of different ways.

Once you have completed all the activities on a particular topic there are some practice questions to try. Again don't be afraid to check your answers as you go by either looking back at some of the activities or even your own notes or textbook. It is far better to put the right answer down having looked at your notes than it is for you to guess incorrectly. The correct answers are all available on our website (**www.ultimate-revision-books.co.uk**).

Once you have done all this try making your own games and activities as this is an even better way of getting you to remember the information. You can convert the summary pages into mind maps or spider diagrams (an example is given at the back of the book). You can also make flash cards with the question on one side and the correct answer on the back (again there is an example of this at the back of the book).

So to recap.
- **Read and make sure you understand the key ideas at the start of each topic.**
- **Work through the different activities, checking the summary pages as you go.**
- **Try the practice questions using your own notes or summary pages to help.**
- **Create your own mind maps, flash cards, games and activities.**

It is recommended that you use a pencil rather than a pen to complete the activities so you can easily correct any mistakes you make.

Unit 1   Rates of Reaction

MEASURING VOLUME OF GAS

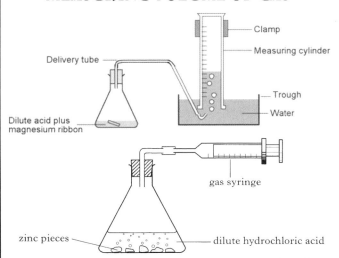

Above are some diagrams of the apparatus you can use to follow a reaction that produces a gas.
You would record how the **volume of gas** changes with time.

MEASURING MASS LOSS

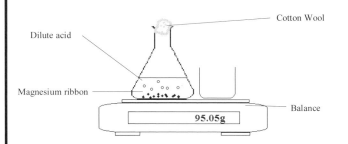

Above is a diagram of the apparatus you can use to follow a reaction that produces a gas.
You would record how the **mass of gas** changes with time.

SPEEDING UP A REACTION

For a reaction to occur, the reactant particles need to collide with a certain amount of energy. Increasing the number of collisions with this energy will speed up a reaction. This can be done by:

- Increasing the concentration.
- Increasing the surface area (turning a solid reactant into a powder).
- Increasing the temperature.
- Adding a catalyst, speeds up certain reactions without getting used up itself.

AVERAGE RATE CALCULATION

Average rate = $\dfrac{\text{change in value}}{\text{time taken}}$

What is the average rate between 10 and 20s for the reaction below?

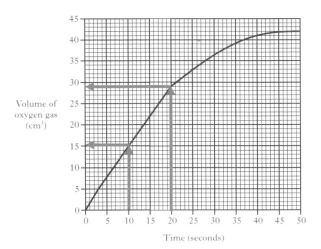

Average rate = $\dfrac{\text{change in volume}}{\text{time}}$

$= \dfrac{29-15}{10}$

$= 1.4 \text{ cm}^3 \text{ s}^{-1}$

Fill in the Blanks

The _____ rate of reaction, is calculated by using the following equation:

$$\text{_____rate} = \frac{\underline{\text{change in mass or volume}}}{\text{_____taken}}$$

You can speed up the reaction between marble lumps and hydrochloric acid by

increasing the _____ area; _____ the

concentration or raising the _____ .

Chemical Misconceptions

Correct the following passage from a student's notebook, circle the incorrect words and write the correct answer in the space below:

The average rate of a reaction is calculated by dividing the time of reaction by the change in volume of gas produced. If you want to speed up the reaction you should increase the surface area by using large pieces of reactants; increase the concentration of the solution by adding more water or heat it up.

_____

_____

_____

_____

_____

_____

_____

Design an Experiment

Using **any** of the pieces of equipment and chemicals given in the box below, design an experiment that could help to measure the average rate of reaction between marble chips and hydrochloric acid and draw a labelled diagram of it in the space below:

beaker	conical flask	balance	measuring cylinder
	gas syringe	marble chips	stopwatch
hydrochloric acid	rubber bung		cotton wool
	delivery tube		

Quiz Word

Answer the following questions to complete the quiz word and then try and work out what the key phrase in the **bold** boxes should be.

1. Increasing this will cause **all** reactions to go quicker. (11)
2. This increases the speed of a reaction by having more reactant particles in a given volume of water. (13)
3. Grinding lumps into powder increases this. (7,4)
4. Increasing the temperature, concentration or surface area will all cause reactions to go ———————. (6)
5. The change in mass or volume of gas produced in a reaction, divided by the time taken will enable you to calculate this. (7,4)
6. Lowering the temperature will cause reactions to go ———————. (6)

Quiz Word Clue: How fast it goes

Shapes of Graphs

A reaction between 2.0g of marble chips and excess 1.0moll^{-1} hydrochloric acid at 25^{0}C produces carbon dioxide gas, the mass of which can be measured. The following graph of mass of gas produced against time was plotted:

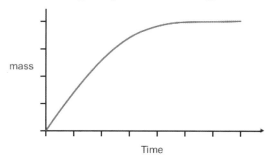

Link the experiment to the shape of graph it is likely to produce. The first has been done for you.

Experiment A:
2.0g marble chips, excess 2.0moll^{-1} hydrochloric acid at 25^{0}C.

Experiment B:
1.0g marble chips, excess 1.0moll^{-1} hydrochloric acid at 25^{0}C.

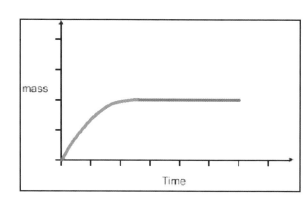

Experiment C:
2.0g marble chips, excess 1.0moll^{-1} hydrochloric acid at 15^{0}C.

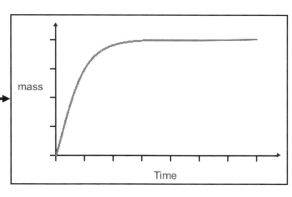

Experiment D:
2.0g marble lumps, excess 1.0moll^{-1} hydrochloric acid at 25^{0}C.

Experiment E:
2.0g marble powder, excess 1.0moll^{-1} hydrochloric acid at 25^{0}C.

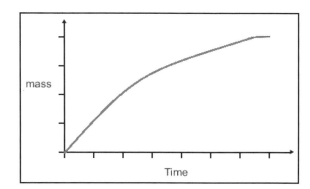

Average Rate Calculations

Below are the results of an experiment where marble chips reacted with hydrochloric acid. The volume of gas was measured every minute for 10 minutes.

Time (min)	Volume of gas (cm^3)
0	0
1	25
2	47
3	70
4	92
5	105
6	114
7	116
8	117
9	118
10	118

Link the section of time to the correct average rate of reaction. The first one has been done for you.

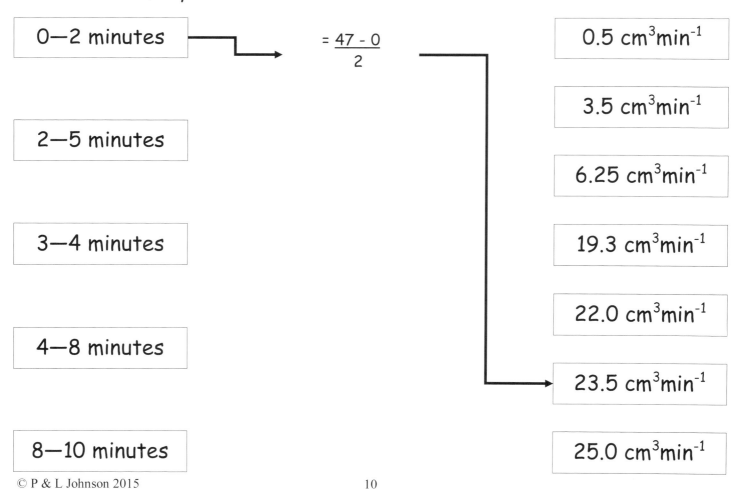

0—2 minutes $= \dfrac{47 - 0}{2}$

0.5 cm^3min^{-1}

2—5 minutes

3.5 cm^3min^{-1}

6.25 cm^3min^{-1}

3—4 minutes

19.3 cm^3min^{-1}

22.0 cm^3min^{-1}

4—8 minutes

23.5 cm^3min^{-1}

8—10 minutes

25.0 cm^3min^{-1}

Practice Questions

1. Egg shell pieces react with dilute hydrochloric acid producing carbon dioxide gas. The rate of reaction between egg shell pieces and dilute hydrochloric acid can be followed by measuring the volume of gas given off during the reaction.

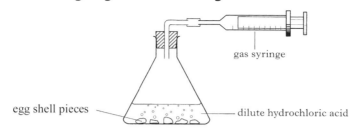

gas syringe

egg shell pieces ——— ——— dilute hydrochloric acid

Results	
Time (seconds)	**Volume of gas (cm^3)**
0	0
10	20
20	40
30	58
40	72
50	80
55	80
60	

a. Plot a line graph of the results of the reaction.

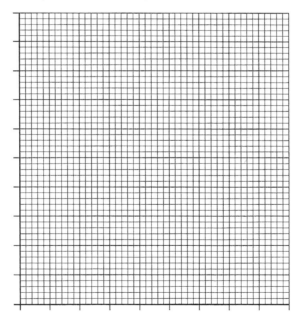

b. Predict the volume of gas that would have been given off after 60 seconds.

c. Calculate the average rate at which gas is given off during the first 40 seconds of the reaction.

_____ cm^{3}s^{-1}

2. Car air bags produce gas in a fraction of a second; involving the decomposition of sodium azide to produce nitrogen gas.

A test experiment using a small quantity of sodium azide lumps produced the following graph of volume of gas produced in cm^3 against time, in milliseconds (ms).

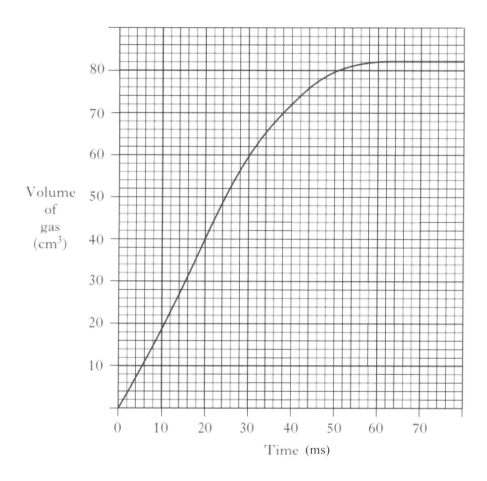

a. Calculate the average rate of the reaction, in cm^3 per millisecond, for the first 20 milliseconds.

_____ cm^3ms^{-1}

b. After how many milliseconds did the reaction finish?

c. Draw a line on the graph to show the shape produced if the same mass of sodium azide powder had been used instead of the lumps.

Unit 1   Atomic Structure

SUB ATOMIC PARTICLES

Particle	Mass (amu)	Charge	Position
proton	1	+	nucleus
neutron	1	0	nucleus
electron	0	-	energy levels

amu = atomic mass units

IMPORTANT NUMBERS

atomic number = number of protons
The number of protons affects the nuclear charge of an atom.

number of protons = number of electrons

mass number = number of protons + neutrons

number of neutrons = mass number-atomic number

ISOTOPES

Elements with the same **atomic number** but **different mass number**.

The difference is due to the atoms having **different numbers of neutrons**.

Relative Atomic Mass (RAM)
Average mass of 100 atoms taking into account the abundance of each isotope.

E.g. chlorine has 2 isotopes
^{35}Cl & ^{37}Cl

The RAM is 35.5 as there is a greater abundance of ^{35}Cl atoms, 75% compared to 25% of ^{37}Cl.

RAM = $\frac{(75 \times 35)+(25 \times 37)}{100}$

= 35.5

NUCLIDE NOTATION

Nuclide notation gives important information about an element.

$^{a}_{b}X$

a = mass number
X = symbol of element
b = atomic number

e.g. $^{23}_{11}Na$

Element	Atomic number	Mass number
sodium	11	23

Number of protons	Number of electrons	Number of neutrons
11	11	12

RELATIVE ATOMIC MASS

When chlorine gas is analysed it is found to have two isotopes, one with a mass of 35 and one with a mass of 37. However there is more of the chlorine 35 than the 37.

e.g. chlorine ^{35}Cl = 75% of all Cl atoms ^{37}Cl = 25% of all Cl atoms

The RELATIVE ATOMIC MASS gives the average mass of all the isotopes taking into account the percentage abundance of each isotope.

RAM = (% abundance of isotope 1 x mass) + (% abundance of isotope 2 x mass)
                                          100

RAM = (75 x 35) + (25 x 37)
                100

RAM = 35.5 a.m.u.

Fill in the Blanks

An atom consists of three types of particle; _____ are positive

charged particles with a mass of _____ a.m.u. found in the nucleus;

neutrons are particles with_____charge found in the _____,

they have a mass of 1_____; electrons have a _____charge,

no mass and are found in _____ _____.

The atomic number is equal to the number of _____ in the

atom. The _____ number is equal to the number of protons and

_____ in the nucleus. _____ are atoms with

the _____atomic number but _____mass

number. The relative atomic mass is the _____mass of all

the isotopes but takes into account their percentage_____.

Quiz Word

Answer the following questions to complete the quiz word and then try and work out what the key phrase in the **bold** boxes should be.

1. A sub atomic particle with no charge. (7)
2. A sub atomic particle found in energy levels. (8)
3. The average mass of an element, taking into account the relative abundance of the different isotopes. (8,6,4)
4. The tiny centre of an atom. (7)
5. A sub atomic particle that makes up the atomic number and part of the mass number. (6)
6. What two atoms with the same atomic number but different mass number are called. (8)

Quiz Word Clue: Another name for the effect of protons in the nucleus

15

Nuclide Notation

Draw lines connecting each nuclide notation to the correct number of protons & neutrons and the correct electron arrangement.

You can use p6 of your data booklet to help. The first one has been done for you.

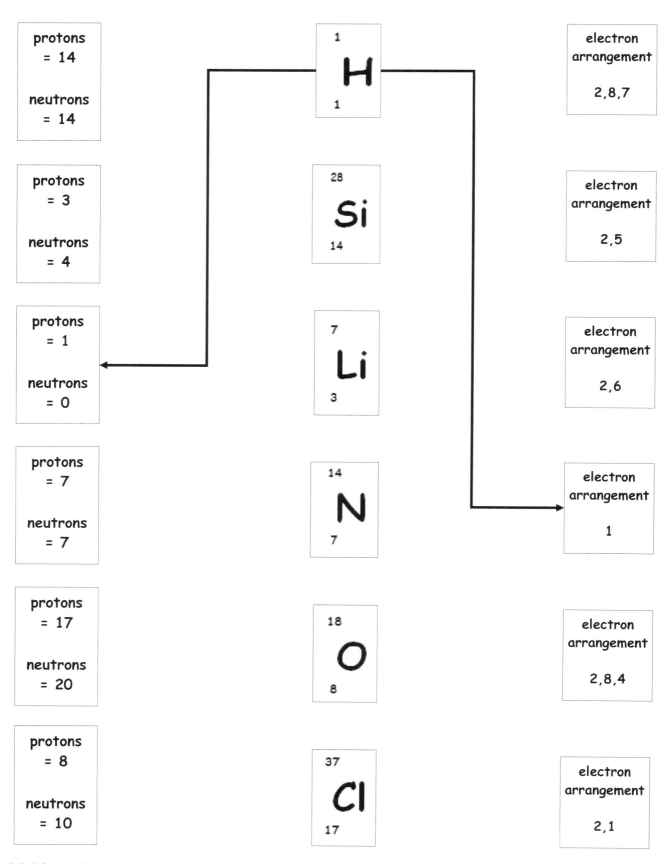

Relative Atomic Mass

Draw lines connecting the element, with its isotopes and their relative abundance, to the correct relative atomic mass.

The first one has been done for you.

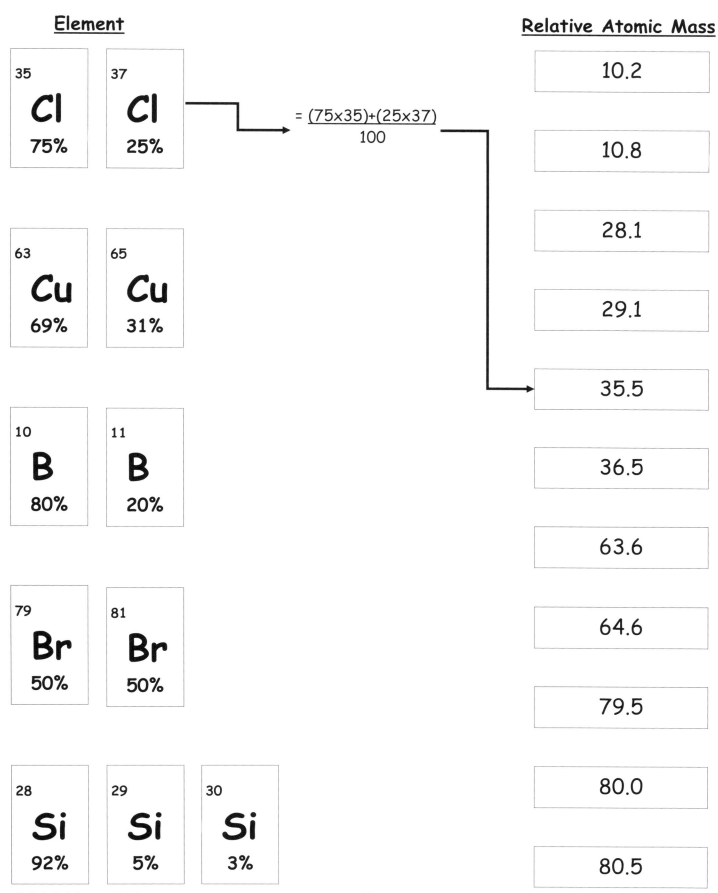

Element

35	37
Cl	Cl
75%	25%

$= \dfrac{(75\times35)+(25\times37)}{100}$

63	65
Cu	Cu
69%	31%

10	11
B	B
80%	20%

79	81
Br	Br
50%	50%

28	29	30
Si	Si	Si
92%	5%	3%

Relative Atomic Mass

10.2

10.8

28.1

29.1

35.5

36.5

63.6

64.6

79.5

80.0

80.5

Most Abundant Isotope

The figure below the scales is the relative atomic mass (RAM) of the element. Looking at the two isotopes and the RAM, decide which isotope is the most abundant and write the nuclide notation for this isotope on the right hand side of the scales. Then put the other isotope on the left hand side of the scales.

The first one has been done for you.

35 **Cl**	37 **Cl**

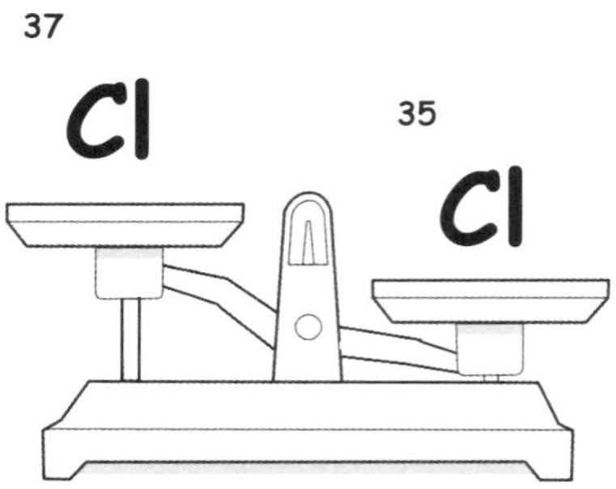

37 **Cl**   35 **Cl**

35.5

6 **Li**	7 **Li**

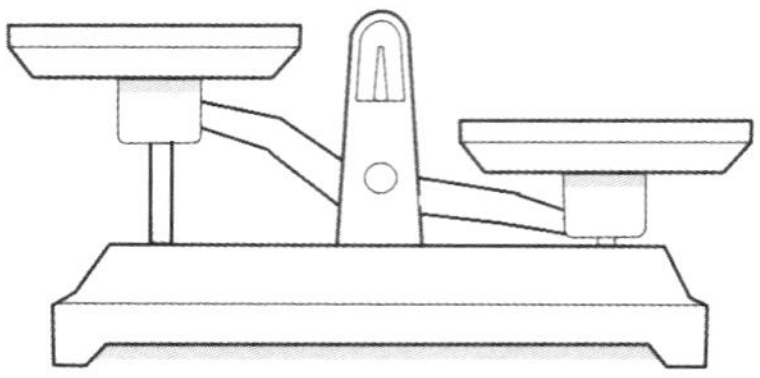

6.9

20 **Ne**	22 **Ne**

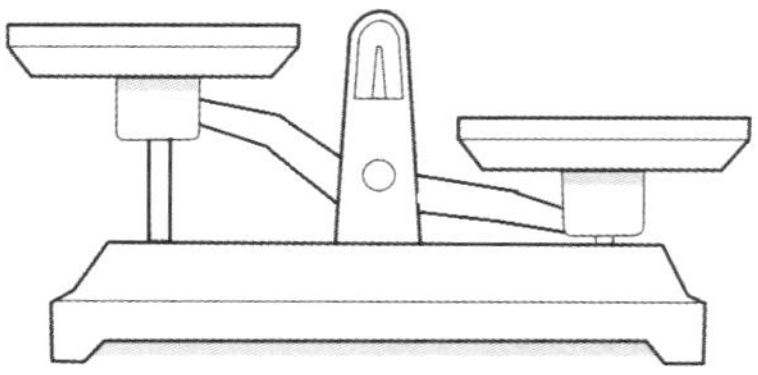

20.2

191 **Ir**	193 **Ir**

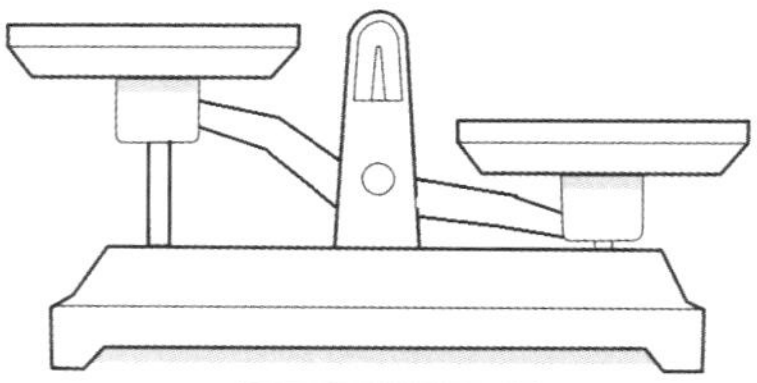

192.3

151 **Eu**	153 **Eu**

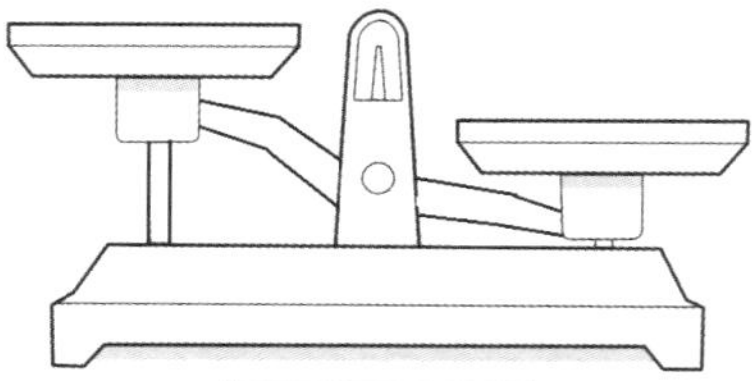

152.2

Practice Questions

1. Potassium is found in bananas. One isotope of potassium is radioactive, it has the following nuclide notation, $^{40}_{19}K$.

a. Complete the table to show the number of particles in an atom of ^{40}K.

Type of particle	Number of particles
proton	
neutron	
electron	

b. How do isotopes of potassium differ from each other?

2a. An isotope of silver has atomic number 47 and mass number 108.

i. Complete the nuclide notation for this isotope of silver.

Ag

ii. How many neutrons are there in this isotope?

b. Silver has two isotopes. One has a mass number of 106 and the other has a mass number of 108.
The relative atomic mass of silver is 107.

What does this tell you about the percentage of each isotope in silver?

3. Carbon is made up of two different types of atom.

a. Complete the table to show the numbers of protons and neutrons in each type of carbon atom.

	Number of protons	Number of neutrons
$^{12}_{6}\text{C}$		
$^{14}_{6}\text{C}$		

b. What term is used to describe the different types of carbon atom?

4. Atoms contain particles called protons, neutrons and electrons.

The nuclide notation of an isotope of neon is shown.

$$^{22}_{10}\text{Ne}$$

Complete the table to show the number of each type of particle in this neon atom.

element	number of protons	number of electrons	number of neutrons
neon			

Unit 1   Bonding & Properties

COVALENT BONDING

Occurs when two or more non-metal atoms share their unpaired outer (valence) electrons.

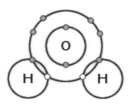

The attraction each nucleus has for the shared pair of electrons holds the atoms together with a **strong** covalent bond.

A common **shape** of carbon compounds is called **tetrahedral**.

IONIC BONDING

Occurs when a metal atom transfers its unpaired outer electrons to a non-metal atom.

This forms a positive metal ion and a negative non-metal ion.

The ions attract each other in all directions and a giant ionic lattice forms.

COVALENT MOLECULAR

- They have a fixed number of atoms in their molecules.
- They have low melting points, as only weak forces of attraction are broken. Bigger molecules have stronger forces of attraction, so have higher melting points. **Substances that are normally gases or liquids are always covalent molecules.**
- They don't conduct electricity in any state.
- They tend to be more soluble in non-aqueous solvents than water, but this can vary.

COVALENT NETWORKS

- There is an unlimited number of atoms in the network, often billions.
- Five main ones; **carbon**, **silicon**, **boron**, **silicon dioxide** and **silicon carbide**.
- They have very high melting points, as strong covalent bonds are being broken.
- They don't conduct in any state (except graphite, which has delocalised electrons).
- They are insoluble in any solvent.

IONIC LATTICES

- They have high melting points, as strong ionic bonds are being broken. All ionic lattices are solid at room temperature
- They do not conduct electricity as solids but can conduct as melts or solutions, as their ions are then free to move.
- They tend to be soluble in water rather than non-aqueous solvents, but this can vary.

Fill in the Blanks

Covalent Molecular:

When two _____ atoms share their unpaired _____ (valence) electrons by overlapping their electron clouds, a covalent bond forms. The attraction of the two positive nuclei for the pair of shared _____ holds the atoms together. If there is a _____ number of atoms in the structure it is known as a covalent molecule. An example would be water (hydrogen oxide), a drop of water will contain billions of individual water _____.

Covalent Network:

When two non-metal atoms share their _____ outer (valence) electrons by overlapping their electron clouds, a _____ bond forms. The attraction of the two positive _____ for the pair of shared electrons holds the atoms together. If there is an unlimited number of _____ in the structure it is known as a covalent network. An example would be sand (silicon dioxide), a grain of sand will contain billions of individual atoms all held together in a single giant _____.

Ionic Lattice:

When metal and _____ atoms transfer their unpaired outer (_____) electrons from the metal atom to the non-metal atom a positive _____ ion and a negative _____ ion form. The oppositely charged ions attract each other and form ionic bonds. As the ions are charged they attract each other in all directions and form a giant ionic _____. An example would be salt (sodium chloride), a grain of salt contains billions of ions in a single giant lattice.

Bonding Type Cards

Using the name of the substance decide what type of bonding it would have. The first one has been done for you.

sodium nitrate	silicon dioxide	carbon chloride	nitrogen hydride
Bonding Type *ionic* *lattice*	Bonding Type	Bonding Type	Bonding Type

iron(III) oxide	silicon carbide	silver(I) bromide	calcium carbonate
Bonding Type	Bonding Type	Bonding Type	Bonding Type

sulfur	carbon (diamond)	silicon	potassium sulfate
Bonding Type	Bonding Type	Bonding Type	Bonding Type

glucose ($C_6H_{12}O_6$)	octane (C_8H_{18})	magnesium phosphate	ammonium chloride
Bonding Type	Bonding Type	Bonding Type	Bonding Type

Bonding Structures

Draw connecting lines from the text to the correct part of the diagrams. The first one has been done for you.

Note: Some of the text may link to two or more parts of the diagrams.

strong covalent bonds

metal ion

weak force of attraction

non-metal atoms

strong ionic bonds

non-metal ion

covalent molecule

covalent network

ionic lattice

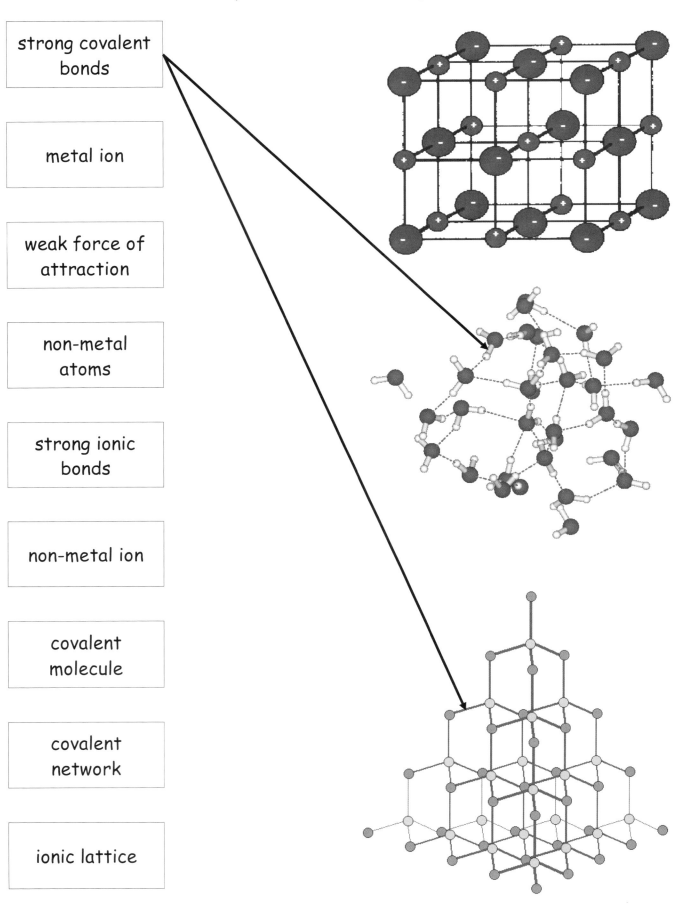

Bonding Properties

Use some of the following possible answers to complete the table below:

Possible Answers
Ionic Lattice   Covalent Network   Covalent Molecule low   high   very high strong covalent bonds   weak forces of attraction strong ionic bonds   conducts only as melt or solution doesn't conduct in any state   insoluble more likely to be soluble   more likely to be insoluble

Property			Ionic Lattice
Melting Point What's broken	very high strong covalent bonds		
Electrical Conductivity		doesn't conduct in any state	
Solubility in Water			

Quiz Word

Answer the following questions to complete the quiz word and then try and work out what the key phrase in the **bold** boxes should be.

1. A bond formed by the sharing of unpaired outer (valence) electrons. (8)
2. The ionic structure formed when billions of oppositely charged ions join together. (8)
3. Ionic substances only do this when molten or in solution. (7)
4. The force of attraction between covalent molecules can be described as being this. (4)
5. Even when the substance is a gas, covalent bonds are always described as being this. (6)
6. The melting point of covalent networks are always this. (4, 4)

Quiz Word Clue: Type of bonding structure

Chemical Misconceptions

Correct the following passage from a student's notebook, circle the incorrect words/phrases and write the correct answer in the space below:

Covalent bonds form between metal and non metal atoms when they share their outer unpaired electrons. When a covalent molecule melts weak covalent bonds are broken. Covalent molecules can conduct electricity as solids, liquids or solutions.

Ionic bonds form when metal and non metal atoms transfer their outer unpaired electrons. Negative metal ions and positive non-metal ions form. Ionic lattices have weak ionic bonds, so have low melting points. Ionic lattices cannot conduct electricity as solids, liquids or solutions.

Lots and lots of substances are covalent networks. They contain a giant structure of billions of atoms held together by weak covalent bonds. They cannot conduct electricity except diamond which has delocalised electrons that are free to move. They have very high melting points as you have to break very strong ionic bonds.

_____

_____

_____

_____

_____

_____

_____

_____

_____

Design an Experiment

Using any of the pieces of equipment and chemicals given in the box below, design an experiment that could help to identify what three unlabelled white powders were. The powders are **marble**, which is calcium carbonate ($CaCO_3$), **zinc chloride** ($ZnCl_2$) and **glucose** ($C_6H_{12}O_6$). You may wish to use p8 of your data booklet to help.

beakers	conical flasks	balance	measuring cylinders
power pack		carbon electrodes	ammeter
hydrochloric acid	water		universal indicator

Bonding Properties

Look at the properties of the substance to decide which type of bonding it will have. The first one has been done for you.

Substance A	Substance B	Substance C
Melting Point	**Melting Point**	**Melting Point**
-46^0C	801^0C	825^0C
Electrical Conductivity	**Electrical Conductivity**	**Electrical Conductivity**
No	As melt & solution	Only as melt
Solubility in H_2O	**Solubility in H_2O**	**Solubility in H_2O**
No	Very	No
Bonding Type	**Bonding Type**	**Bonding Type**
covalent molecular		

Substance D	Substance E	Substance F
Melting Point	**Melting Point**	**Melting Point**
1713^0C	115^0C	3825^0C
Electrical Conductivity	**Electrical Conductivity**	**Electrical Conductivity**
No	No	Yes as a solid
Solubility in H_2O	**Solubility in H_2O**	**Solubility in H_2O**
No	No	No
Bonding Type	**Bonding Type**	**Bonding Type**

Substance G	Substance H	Substance I
Melting Point	**Melting Point**	**Melting Point**
550^0C	114^0C	2614^0C
Electrical Conductivity	**Electrical Conductivity**	**Electrical Conductivity**
As melt & solution	No	As melt & solution
Solubility in H_2O	**Solubility in H_2O**	**Solubility in H_2O**
Yes	Poor	Yes
Bonding Type	**Bonding Type**	**Bonding Type**

Unknown Substances

There are 10 substances labelled from A to J.

The substances are copper chloride, silicon dioxide (sand), sugar ($C_{12}H_{22}O_{11}$), copper carbonate, oxygen, pentane (C_5H_{12}), sodium chloride, nickel chloride, hydrogen and calcium carbonate (marble).

Using the information given in the table and your data booklet complete the table, identifying each substance and their bonding type, using the letters **CM** for covalent molecular, **CN** for covalent network and **IL** for ionic lattice.

Substance	Melting point (^0C)	Properties	Name	Bonding type
A	>1000	White solid, soluble in water, conducts as a solution producing chlorine gas.		
B	>300	Green solid, soluble in water, conducts as a solution producing chlorine gas.		
C	>100	White solid, soluble in water, doesn't conduct electricity in any state.		
D	>300	Green solid, insoluble in water, doesn't conduct as a solution. Reacts with an acid producing carbon dioxide gas.		
E	>-140	Liquid that doesn't conduct electricity, is insoluble and immiscible in water.		
F	>1000	Light brown solid, insoluble in water and doesn't conduct electricity in any state.		
G	>300	Blue solid, soluble in water, conducts as a solution producing chlorine gas and a brown solid.		
H	>1000	White solid, insoluble in water, doesn't conduct as a solution. Reacts with an acid producing carbon dioxide gas.		
I	<-200	Colourless gas that burns with a pop.		
J	<-200	Colourless gas that relights a glowing splint.		

Practice Questions

1. During house fires plastics, such as PVC, burn and can produce dangerous chemicals such as hydrogen chloride gas.

   Draw a diagram to show how the **outer** electrons are shared in a molecule of hydrogen chloride.

2. The element silicon can exist in the compound silicon carbide, called carborundum, a very hard solid used to sharpen knives.
   The structure of carborundum is shown in the diagram.

   a. Name the type of **bonding** and **structure** present in carborundum.

   b. Like carbon, silicon forms many compounds with hydrogen to form compounds similar to alkanes, the simplest is called silane, SiH_4.

   i. Draw a diagram to show how the outer electrons are arranged in a molecule of silane, SiH_4.

   ii. Draw a diagram to show the **shape** of a molecule of silane, SiH_4.

3. The properties of a substance depend on its type of bonding and structure. There are three types of bonding and structure given in the table below:

Covalent molecular	Covalent network	Ionic lattice

a. Complete the table to match up each type of bonding and structure with its properties.

Type of bonding & structure	Properties
	do not conduct electricity and have very high melting points
	have high melting points and conduct electricity when liquid but not when solid
	do not conduct electricity and have low melting points

b. Three white solid powders all look exactly the same. They are sodium chloride (salt), calcium carbonate (chalk) and sucrose (sugar). Use your knowledge of the substances and your data booklet to help complete the table below by circling the correct response.

Substance	Melting point	Solubility in water	Conductivity as a melt
sodium chloride	high / low	soluble / insoluble	conducts / doesn't conduct
calcium carbonate	high / low	soluble / insoluble	conducts / doesn't conduct
sucrose	high / low	soluble / insoluble	conducts / doesn't conduct

Unit 1 Chemical Formulae

CROSSING OVER THE VALENCY

The valency is the number of unpaired outer electrons that an atom has.
For groups 1-4 the valency is the same as the group number; for groups 5-7 the valency is 8 minus the group number.
This is the method used to work out chemical formulae

1. Write symbol for elements.
2. Put valency above each symbol.
3. Cross over and down the number.
4. Simplify.

e.g. carbon oxide

$$\overset{4}{C} \diagdown \diagup \overset{2}{O}$$

CO_2 $\underset{2}{} \underset{4}{}$

Exceptions:
Names with prefixes **tell you** the formula and they do not need to be worked out or simplified:
carbon monoxide = CO
sulfur trioxide = SO_3
dinitrogen tetroxide = N_2O_4

ROMAN NUMERALS

Transition metals and metals in higher groups can have more than one valency. Roman numerals are used to tell you the valency of the metal.
Use crossing over the valency as before to work out the formula:
e.g iron(III) oxide

$$\overset{3}{Fe} \diagdown \diagup \overset{2}{O}$$
$$\underset{2}{} \underset{3}{}$$

$$Fe_2O_3$$

DIATOMIC ELEMENTS

The following elements are always diatomic when as elements on their own:
Br_2, O_2, F_2, I_2, N_2, Cl_2, & H_2
Remember them as BOFINCH
OR GENINE (all elements ending in -gen or -ine)

IONIC FORMULAE

To convert to an **ionic formula** use the valency to work out the size of the charge and remember the metal is always positive and the non-metal negative.
Use brackets if there is more than one ion.

e.g. Fe_2O_3
becomes $(Fe^{3+})_2 (O^{2-})_3$

GROUP IONS

Ions containing more than one element are called group ions.
Their names, formulae and valencies are found on p8 of the data booklet.
Use crossing over the valency as before to work out the formula, but use brackets if there is more than one group ion in the formula:

e.g. magnesium nitrate

$$\overset{2}{Mg} \diagdown \diagup \overset{1}{NO_3}$$
$$\underset{1}{} \underset{2}{}$$

$$Mg(NO_3)_2$$

Or $Mg^{2+} (NO_3^-)_2$

What's in a Name?

Chemical names tell us what elements are present in the compound.
Connect the name to the elements present in the compound, use p8 of your data booklet to help. The first one has been done for you.

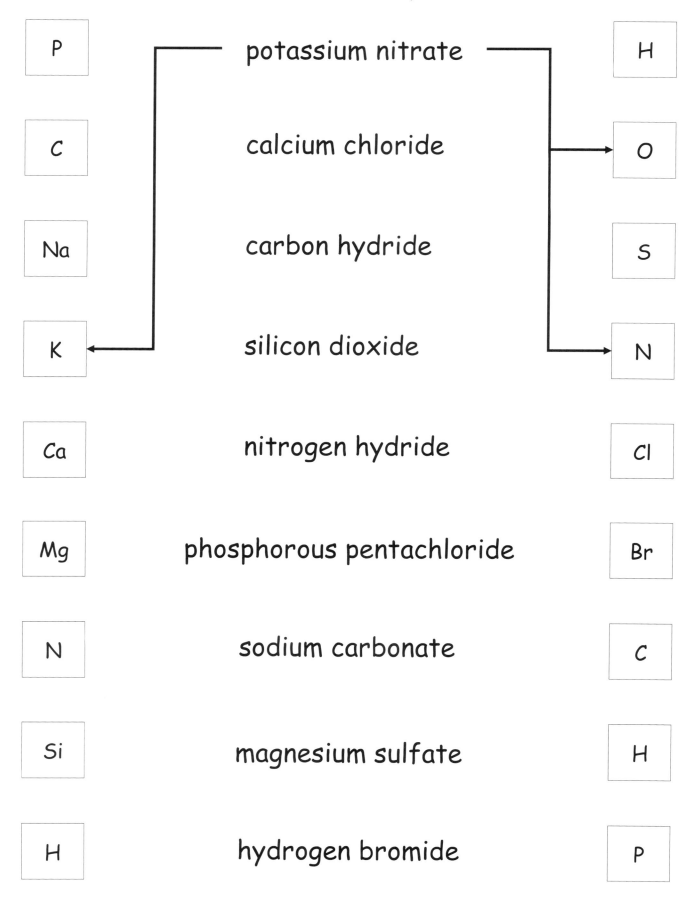

P	potassium nitrate	H
C	calcium chloride	O
Na	carbon hydride	S
K	silicon dioxide	N
Ca	nitrogen hydride	Cl
Mg	phosphorous pentachloride	Br
N	sodium carbonate	C
Si	magnesium sulfate	H
H	hydrogen bromide	P

Valency

The valency is the number of unpaired outer electrons that an atom has.

For groups 1-4 the valency is the same as the group number; for groups 5-7 the valency is 8 minus the group number.

Complete the following table:

Group Number	1	2	3	4	5	6	7
Valency							

Connect the element to its valency

Draw connecting lines from the element, with its electron arrangement shown, to its correct valency. The first one has been done for you.

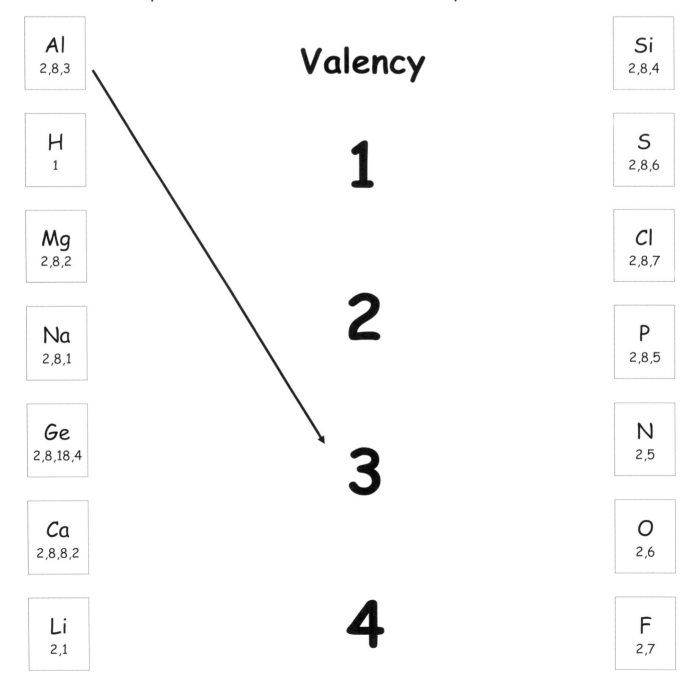

Chemical Formulae

The chemical formula of a compound is worked out by crossing over the valencies and then simplifying the numbers.

Draw connecting lines from the compound shown to its correct chemical formula. You will need to use your data booklet to help. The first one has been done for you.

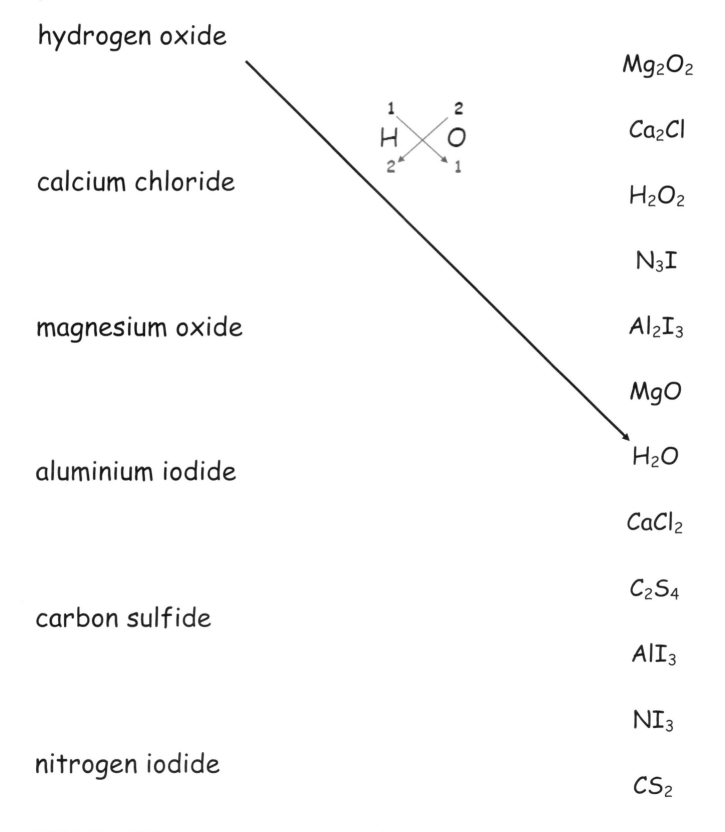

hydrogen oxide

Mg_2O_2

Ca_2Cl

calcium chloride

H_2O_2

N_3I

magnesium oxide

Al_2I_3

MgO

aluminium iodide

H_2O

$CaCl_2$

C_2S_4

carbon sulfide

AlI_3

NI_3

nitrogen iodide

CS_2

Chemical Misconceptions

A student has completed an exercise on working out chemical formulae. They got exactly half of the questions wrong! Work out which ones they got wrong and write the correct answer in the space at the side.

1/ sulfur trioxide $\qquad$ SO_3

2/ nitrogen dioxide $\qquad$ N_2O_3

3/ silicon dioxide $\qquad$ SiO_2

4/ sodium oxide $\qquad$ Na_2O_2

5/ magnesium nitride $\qquad$ MgN

6/ calcium oxide $\qquad$ CaO_2

7/ lithium bromide $\qquad$ $LiBr$

8/ sulfur chloride $\qquad$ SCl_2

9/ oxygen $\qquad$ O

10/ hydrogen $\qquad$ H_2

11/ iron (III) oxide $\qquad$ FE_2O_3

12/ copper (II) oxide $\qquad$ Cu_2O_2

13/ tin (IV) chloride $\qquad$ $SnCl_4$

14/ lithium sulfate $\qquad$ Li_2SO_4

15/ calcium carbonate $\qquad$ Ca_3CO_2

16/ ammonium dichromate $(NH_4)_2Cr_2O_7$

Ionic Formulae

Chemical formulae for ionic compounds can be converted into ionic formulae by showing the charge on the ions. Remember to put ions in brackets if there is more than one of them.

Link the chemical formula or chemical name to the correct ionic formula. The first one has been done for you.

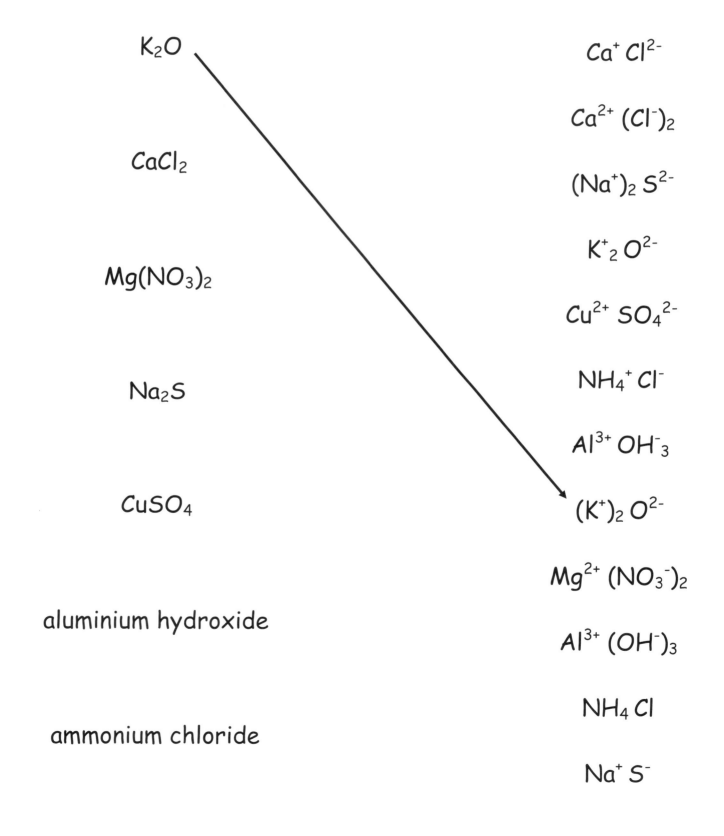

K_2O

$CaCl_2$

$Mg(NO_3)_2$

Na_2S

$CuSO_4$

aluminium hydroxide

ammonium chloride

$Ca^+ Cl^{2-}$

$Ca^{2+} (Cl^-)_2$

$(Na^+)_2 S^{2-}$

$K^+_2 O^{2-}$

$Cu^{2+} SO_4^{2-}$

$NH_4^+ Cl^-$

$Al^{3+} OH^-_3$

$(K^+)_2 O^{2-}$

$Mg^{2+} (NO_3^-)_2$

$Al^{3+} (OH^-)_3$

$NH_4 Cl$

$Na^+ S^-$

Ionic Charges

The charge on transition metal ions can be found by using the Periodic Table to workout the charge or valency of the non metal ion then uncrossing over the formula. Draw connecting lines from the compound shown to the correct transition metal ion. You will want to use your data booklet to help. The first one has been done for you.

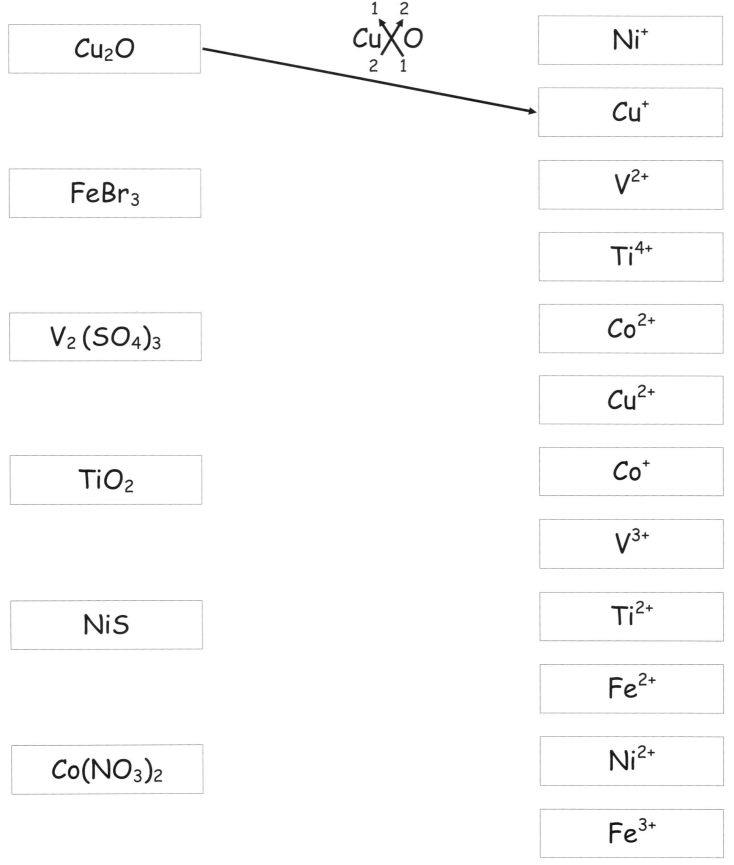

Quiz Word

Answer the following questions to complete the quiz word and then try and work out what the key phrase in the **bold** boxes should be.

1. Involved in all bonds and used to work out the chemical formula. (8,5,9)
2. Genine and BOFINCH are used to remember these elements. (8)
3. Another name for the number of clue 1. (7)
4. Done to 3, as part of the process to work out a chemical formula. (5,4)

Practice Questions

1. Silica gel packets are used to absorb moisture in the packaging of expensive electronic equipment.

a. What is the chemical formula of silicon dioxide?

b. Calcium chloride is a white solid that can do the same job as silica gels.

   Write the **ionic formula** for calcium chloride.

2. Rust is hydrated iron oxide and it has the familiar red colour due to the presence of the iron ion. The formula for the iron oxide found in rust is Fe_2O_3.

a. What is the charge on the iron ion that causes the red colour of rust?

b. During the initial formation of rust, iron(II) hydroxide forms. Write the ionic formula for iron(II) hydroxide.

3. Zinc phosphate is used as a corrosion treatment for metals against hydrogen sulphide, oxygen and carbon dioxide.

a. What is the charge on the zinc ion in the compound zinc phosphate $Zn_3(PO_4)_2$?

b. Write the chemical formula of hydrogen sulphide.

Unit 1   Reaction Quantities

THE MOLE

In chemistry we compare amounts of substances using the mole.

Like a dozen it is simply a fixed number of something.

For solids, liquids & gases:

Number of moles = $\frac{\text{mass of substance}}{\text{gram formula mass}}$

$$n = \frac{m}{GFM}$$

For solutions:

Number of moles = concentration x volume

$$n = cv \qquad \text{where v is in litres}$$

GRAM FORMULA MASS

The GFM is the mass of one mole of a substance expressed in grams.

e.g. H_2O
   1×16
   2×1
   $\underline{18g}$

The relative atomic mass of each atom of each element in the formula is added together.

e.g. $(NH_4)_2SO_4$
   4×16
   1×32
   8×1
   2×14
   $\underline{132g}$

BALANCED CHEMICAL EQUATIONS

This is an equation that has the same number of atoms of each type of element on both sides of the equation.

To balance an equation you should only change the number of moles of a substance and not its chemical formula.

$2\,H_2 \quad + \quad O_2 \rightarrow 2\,H_2O$
H=2x2=4   H = 2x2=4
O=2   O = 1x2=2
$2H_2 \quad + \quad O_2 \rightarrow 2H_2O$

USING BALANCED CHEMICAL EQUATIONS

It is possible to use a balanced chemical equation to work out how much product is produced during a chemical reaction or how much reactant is needed to produce a certain amount of product.

If 32g of methane (CH_4) is burnt, how much water is formed?

	$CH_4 +$	$2O_2$	$\rightarrow$	CO_2	$+$	$2H_2O$	$2H_2O$
If	1 mole		produces			2moles	↳ 2x16
	16g		⟺			36g	→ 4x1
	1g		⟺			$\dfrac{36}{16}$	36
							CH_4
	32g		⟺			$\dfrac{36}{16} \times 32$	↳ 4x1
							→ 1x12
						$\underline{72g}$	16

Another way of tackling this question is to use mole calculations:

$CH_4 + \quad 2O_2 \quad \rightarrow \quad CO_2 \quad + \quad 2H_2O$

$\;1\;\; : \quad 2 \quad\;\; : \quad 1 \quad\;\; : \quad 2$

m= 32g   m=? CH_4

$n = \dfrac{m}{GFM}$

$n = \dfrac{32}{16}$

↳ 4x1
→ 1x12
16

$n = 2$ ⟶ $n = 2 \times 2$ H_2O

$m = n \times GFM$ ↳ 1x16

$m = 4 \times 18$ → 2x1

$m = \underline{72g}$ 18

Note the GFM of the H_2O is for just 1 mole.

Both methods work and produce exactly the same answer. Your teacher will have probably taught you one of these methods.

Gram Formula Mass

The gram formula mass is calculated by adding up the atomic masses of all the atoms of the elements in the chemical formula.

Draw connecting lines from the compound shown to its correct gram formula mass. You will want to use your data booklet to help. The first one has been done for you.

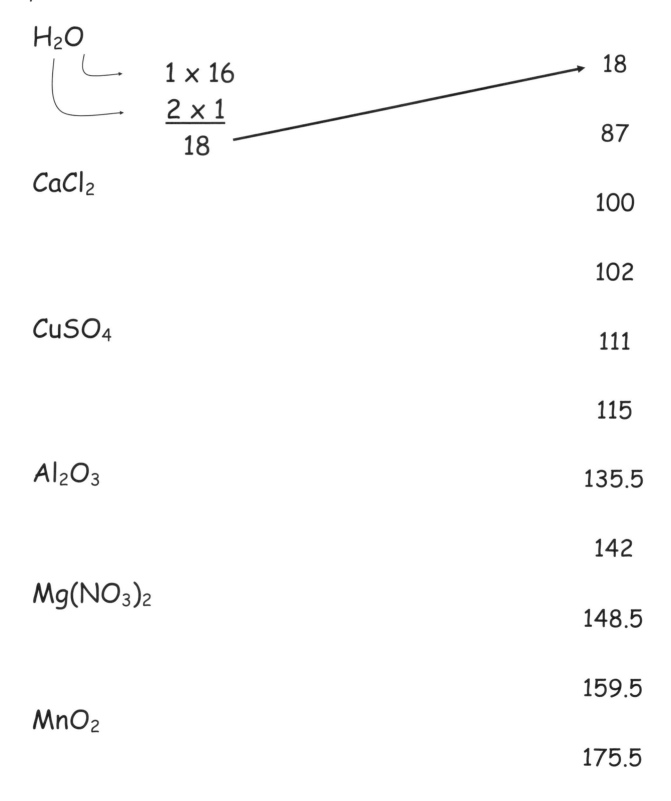

H_2O

1×16

$\underline{2 \times 1}$

18

18

$CaCl_2$

87

100

102

$CuSO_4$

111

115

Al_2O_3

135.5

142

$Mg(NO_3)_2$

148.5

159.5

MnO_2

175.5

Numbers of Moles

You can calculate the number of moles of a substance by using either:

$$n = \frac{mass}{GFM} \qquad\qquad or \qquad\qquad n = cv$$

(Remember volume is in litres)

Draw connecting lines from the compound shown to its number of moles, you may use your answers for the gram formula mass from the previous page. The first one has been done for you.

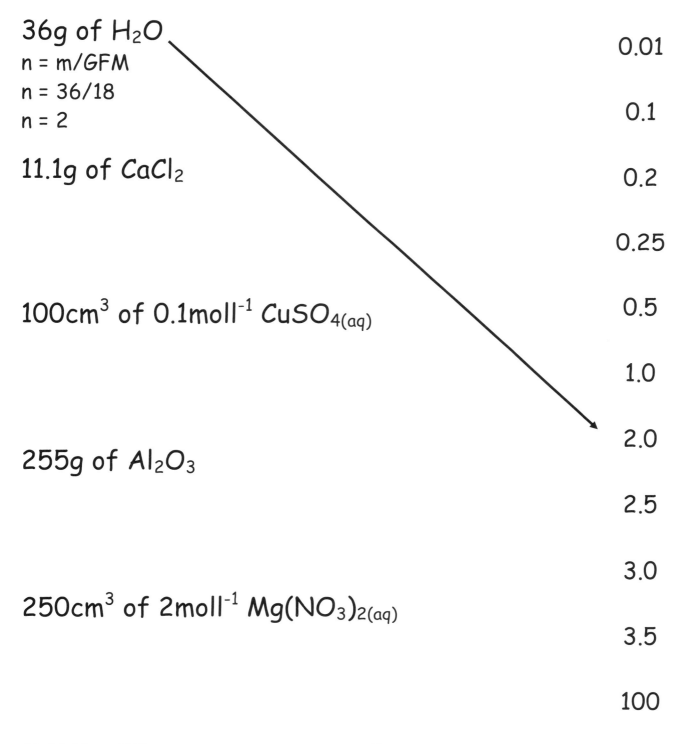

36g of H_2O

n = m/GFM
n = 36/18
n = 2

11.1g of $CaCl_2$

100cm^3 of 0.1moll^{-1} $CuSO_{4(aq)}$

255g of Al_2O_3

250cm^3 of 2moll^{-1} $Mg(NO_3)_{2(aq)}$

0.01

0.1

0.2

0.25

0.5

1.0

2.0

2.5

3.0

3.5

100

Chemical Misconceptions

A student has completed an exercise on working out numbers of moles. They got every one wrong but fortunately showed their working out. Circle the part they got wrong and then work out what the correct answer should have been:

Q1   Calculate the number of moles of each substance, show your working out.

a.   25g of $CaCO_3$

$$n = m/GFM \qquad CaCO_3$$
$$= 25/68 \qquad\qquad 16+12+40 = 68$$
$$= 0.37$$

b.   72g of H_2O

$$n = m/GFM \qquad H_2O$$
$$= 72 \times 18 \qquad\qquad 2+16 = 18$$
$$= 1296$$

c.   6.4g of oxygen gas

$$n = m/GFM \qquad O$$
$$= 6.4/16 \qquad\qquad = 16$$
$$= 0.4$$

d.   2litres of a $2moll^{-1}$ solution of $CuSO_4$

$$n = m/GFM \qquad CuSO_4$$
$$= 2/159.5 \qquad\qquad 63.5+32+64 = 159.5$$
$$= 0.0125$$

e. $250cm^3$ of a $0.2moll^{-1}$ solution of sodium chloride

$$n = C/V$$
$$= 0.2/0.25$$
$$= 0.8$$

f. $50cm^3$ of a $0.1moll^{-1}$ solution of hydrochloric acid.

$$n = C \, V$$
$$= 0.1 \times 50$$
$$= 5.0$$

Quiz Word

Answer the following questions to complete the quiz word and then try and work out what the key phrase in the **bold** boxes should be.

1. Mass of one mole of a substance. (4,7,4)
2. A chemical measure of the amount of a substance. (4)
3. Needed to calculate the number of moles of a solution. (6)
4. When the number of atoms of each element is the same on both sides of a chemical equation. (8)
5. Need to convert cm^3 into this when calculating numbers of moles of solutions. (6)

Quiz Word Clue: Needed to compare quantities of chemicals

Balanced Chemical Equations

To balance a chemical equation you need to count the number of atoms of each element on both sides of the arrow sign. You can then only change the number of molecules of each to ensure that the number of atoms of each element are the same on both sides.

In the example below hydrogen and oxygen molecules react to form water.

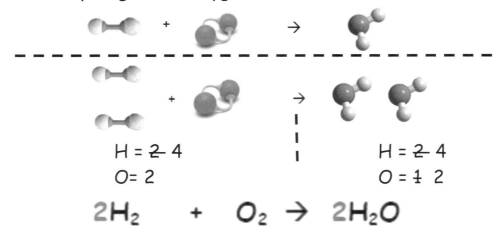

$$H = \cancel{2} \; 4$$
$$O = 2$$

$$H = \cancel{2} \; 4$$
$$O = \cancel{1} \; 2$$

$$2H_2 \;\; + \;\; O_2 \;\; \rightarrow \;\; 2H_2O$$

Use the molymod pictures below to help balance the following equations:

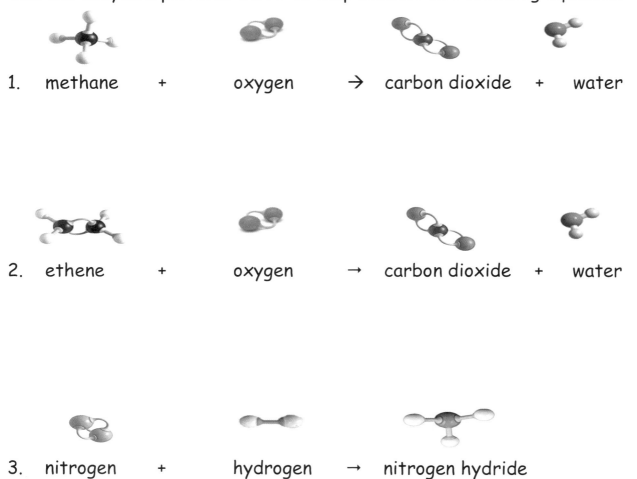

1.   methane   +   oxygen   →   carbon dioxide   +   water

2.   ethene   +   oxygen   →   carbon dioxide   +   water

3.   nitrogen   +   hydrogen   →   nitrogen hydride

Practice Questions

1. Many plants with edible leaves, such as wood sorrel, contain oxalic acid, $C_2H_2O_4$, which has a sharp bitter taste.

    The quantity of oxalic acid in a plant can be analysed by using the reaction of oxalic acid with an oxidising agent such as potassium permanganate.

    A handful of wood sorrel leaves was found to contain 2.7g of oxalic acid.

    How many moles of oxalic acid, $C_2H_2O_4$, are contained in 2.7g?
    (Formula mass of oxalic acid = 90)

    _____

2. At the start of the 20th Century ammonia was primarily made by the reaction of ammonium compounds with an alkali such as sodium hydroxide:

    $$NH_4Cl_{(s)} + NaOH_{(s)} \rightarrow NH_{3(g)} + NaCl + H_2O_{(g)}$$

    What mass of ammonium chloride, NH_4Cl, would be needed to make 34 kg of ammonia, NH_3?

    _____kg

3a.   Write the chemical formula for cobalt(II) nitrate.

b.   Calculate the number of moles of solute contained in $250cm^3$ of 0.2 moll^{-1} colbalt(II) nitrate solution.

_____

4.   Solid fuel rocket boosters often use ammonium perchlorate as the source of oxygen for their combustion reaction.

   $NH_4ClO_{4(s)}$ $\rightarrow$ $NH_4Cl_{(s)}$ + $2O_{2(g)}$

Calculate the mass of oxygen produced when 1000g of ammonium perchlorate completely decomposes.

_____ g

5.	Sulfuric acid is one of the most common acids manufactured in the UK. The initial stage of its manufacture uses the Contact Process to convert sulfur dioxide to sulfur trioxide:

$$SO_{2(g)} \quad + \quad O_{2(g)} \quad \rightarrow \quad SO_{3(g)}$$

a.	Balance this equation.

b.	The next stage involves the reaction of sulfur trioxide with water to produce sulfuric acid:

$$SO_{3(g)} \quad + \quad H_2O_{(l)} \quad \rightarrow \quad H_2SO_{4(aq)}$$

Calculate the mass of sulfur trioxide that would react completely with 1800kg of water.

_____ kg

6.	Potassium permanganate is a powerful oxidising agent and is an important chemical in many analytical techniques.

	It is made by reacting manganese dioxide with potassium hydroxide, in the presence of oxygen.

$$4MnO_{2(s)} + 4KOH_{(s)} + 3O_{2(g)} \rightarrow 4KMnO_{4(s)} + 2H_2O_{(g)}$$

	What mass of potassium permanganate can be made from 348kg of manganese dioxide?

_____ kg

Unit 1 Acids & Bases

IONS PRESENT

Non-metal oxides can dissolve in water to form **acids**; **metal oxides** can dissolve in water to form **alkalis**.

Common Examples of acids & alkalis:

hydrochloric acid	HCl	$H^+ + Cl^-$
sulfuric acid	H_2SO_4	$2H^+ + SO_4^{2-}$
nitric acid	HNO_3	$H^+ + NO_3^-$
sodium hydroxide	NaOH	$Na^+ + OH^-$
calcium hydroxide	$Ca(OH)_2$	$Ca^{2+} + 2OH^-$
ammonium hydroxide	NH_4OH	$NH_4^+ + OH^-$

pH

All acids contain aqueous H^+ ions.
All alkalis contain aqueous OH^- ions.

$$H_2O \rightleftharpoons H^+ + OH^-$$

Water can dissociate and contains an equal number of H^+ and OH^- ions, pH=7.

Acids have more H^+ than OH^- ions, pH<7

Alkalis have more OH^- than H^+ ions, pH>7

NEUTRALISATION

Acids can be neutralised by bases; either metal hydroxides (alkalis), metal oxides or metal carbonates. As they are neutralised the pH rises towards 7.

A salt & water is always produced; a metal carbonate produces $CO_{2(g)}$ as well.

A salt is formed from the positive ion of the base and the negative ion of the acid.

sodium + hydro**chloric** → **sodium** + water
hydroxide   acid   **chloride**

NaOH + HCl → NaCl + H_2O

TITRATIONS

A titration can be used to calculate experimentally the concentration of an acid or alkali. At the end point the number of moles of H^+ ions must equal number of moles of OH^- ions.

number moles acid = number moles alkali

We know n = CV
but we need to take into account some acids have more than one H^+ ion and some alkalis have more than one OH^- ion.

So $PVC_{acid} = PVC_{alkali}$

Where P = number of H^+ or OH^- in the formula of the acid and alkali.

Below is the apparatus used in a titration:

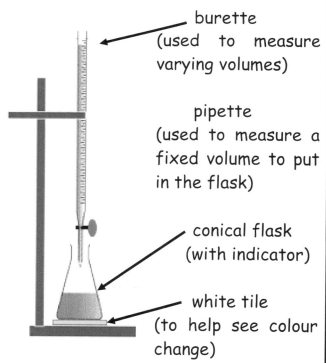

burette
(used to measure varying volumes)

pipette
(used to measure a fixed volume to put in the flask)

conical flask
(with indicator)

white tile
(to help see colour change)

Titrations are repeated until two results are concordant, they are within $0.2cm^3$ of one another, an average of these is then calculated to get the average titre.

Formulae of acids and alkalis

Match the acid and alkali names with their formula and ions present. The first one has been done for you.

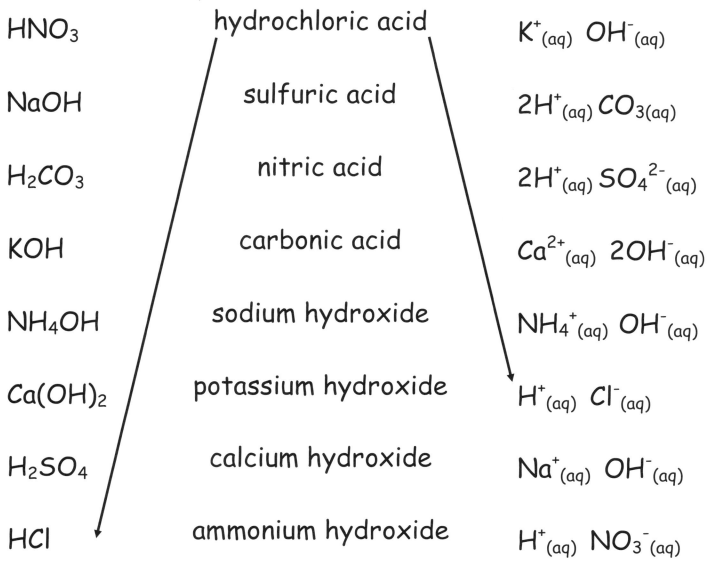

HNO₃	hydrochloric acid	K⁺(aq) OH⁻(aq)
NaOH	sulfuric acid	2H⁺(aq) CO₃(aq)
H₂CO₃	nitric acid	2H⁺(aq) SO₄²⁻(aq)
KOH	carbonic acid	Ca²⁺(aq) 2OH⁻(aq)
NH₄OH	sodium hydroxide	NH₄⁺(aq) OH⁻(aq)
Ca(OH)₂	potassium hydroxide	H⁺(aq) Cl⁻(aq)
H₂SO₄	calcium hydroxide	Na⁺(aq) OH⁻(aq)
HCl	ammonium hydroxide	H⁺(aq) NO₃⁻(aq)

Fill in the Blanks

All acids contain aqueous _____ ions, whereas all _____ contain aqueous OH⁻ ions. When an acid is diluted or neutralised the concentration of _____ ions decreases and its pH moves _____ pH 7. When an alkali is _____ or _____ its concentration of OH⁻ ions _____ and its pH moves towards pH 7. Acidic solutions contain _____ H⁺ ions than OH⁻ ions. Alkaline solutions contain more _____ ions than _____ ions. Neutral solutions contain _____ concentrations of both H⁺ ions and OH⁻ ions.

Salts

Connect the correct acid and base cards to form the salt cards in the middle. The first one has been done for you.

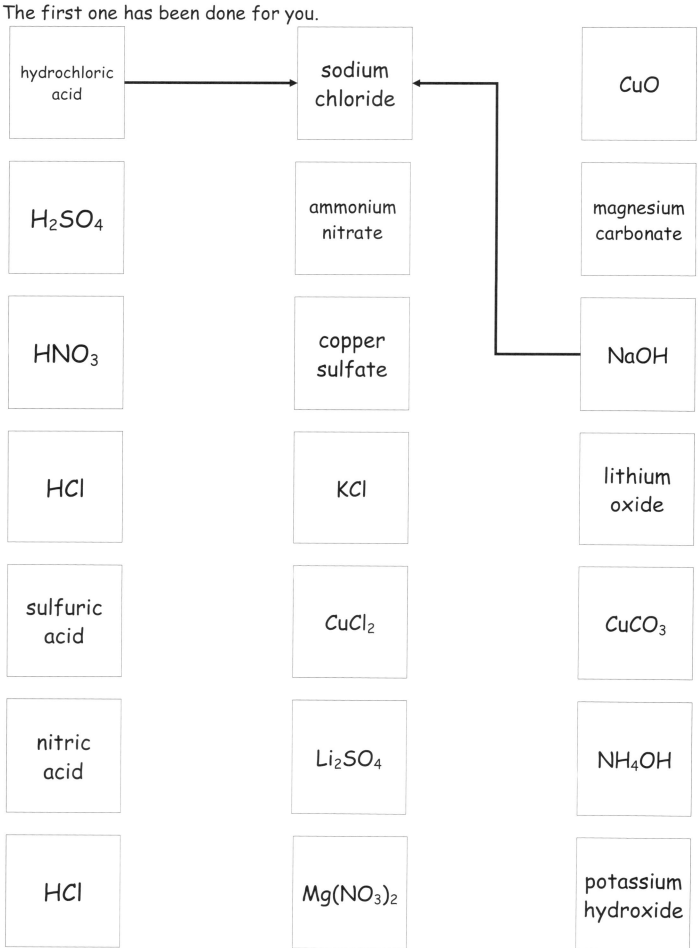

hydrochloric acid	sodium chloride	CuO
H₂SO₄	ammonium nitrate	magnesium carbonate
HNO₃	copper sulfate	NaOH
HCl	KCl	lithium oxide
sulfuric acid	CuCl₂	CuCO₃
nitric acid	Li₂SO₄	NH₄OH
HCl	Mg(NO₃)₂	potassium hydroxide

Quiz Word

Answer the following questions to complete the quiz word and then try and work out what the key word in the **bold** boxes should be.

1. The ion present in all acid solutions. (8)
2. This is added to identify the end point of a titration. (9)
3. The technique used to calculate the concentration of an acid or alkali. (9)
4. A substance always produced by the reaction between an acid and base. (4)
5. Type of metal compound that can neutralise an acid. (5)
6. Type of metal compound that forms carbon dioxide during a reaction with an acid. (9)

Design an Experiment

Using any of the pieces of equipment and chemicals given in the box below, design an experiment that could make a pure and dry sample of copper(II) sulfate.

beakers	filter paper	evaporating basin
filter funnel	measuring cylinders	copper(II) carbonate
water	Bunsen burner	copper(II) oxide
hydrochloric acid	sulfuric acid	nitric acid
dropping pipette	universal indicator	pH paper

Chemical Misconceptions

A student has written a plan for completing a titration, including a labelled diagram, below. They have made a number of errors, can you spot them all and change them so that their notes are correct.

Method

1. Measure out exactly 25.0cm³ of the acid with unknown concentration using a measuring cylinder.
2. Pour it into a beaker and add a few drops of indicator.
3. Set up a burette by filling it with 0.1moll⁻¹ sodium hydroxide solution.
4. Place the beaker on a black tile so that the colour of the indicator can be clearly seen.
5. Slowly add the sodium hydroxide into the conical flask without swirling.
6. Note the volume when the indicator changes colour.
7. Repeat but this time only adding the sodium hydroxide a drop at a time near to the end-point.
8. Repeat until you get concordant results, which are results within 2cm³ of each other.

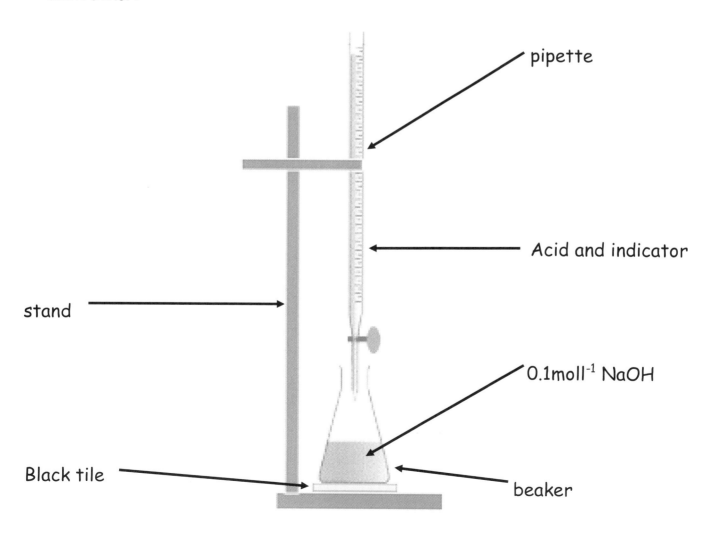

pipette

Acid and indicator

stand

0.1moll⁻¹ NaOH

Black tile

beaker

Practice Questions

1. pH is related to concentration of hydrogen ions in the solution.

Concentration (moll^{-1})	1.0	0.1	0.01
pH	0	1	2

Predict the concentration of hydrochloric acid solution with a pH of 4.

_____ moll^{-1}

2. Lithium salts can be made by two different types of reaction.

a. Lithium phosphate can be made by reacting solutions of lithium chloride and sodium phosphate.
The ionic equation for this reaction is:

$3Li^+_{(aq)} + 3Cl^-_{(aq)} + 3Na^+_{(aq)} + PO_4^{3-}_{(aq)} \rightarrow (Li^+)_3 PO_4^{3-}_{(s)} + 3Na^+_{(aq)} + 3Cl^-_{(aq)}$

i. Rewrite the equation omitting spectator ions.

ii. Name the type of reaction taking place.

b. Lithium sulphate can be made by titrating sulphuric acid with lithium hydroxide solution, followed by evaporation.

C = 0.1
v = 0.02

C = ?
v = 0.0185L

$2LiOH_{(aq)} + H_2SO_{4(aq)} \rightarrow Li_2SO_{4(aq)} + 2H_2O_{(l)}$

If 18.5cm^3 of dilute sulphuric acid were required to neutralise 20cm^3 of 0.1moll^{-1} lithium hydroxide solution, calculate the concentration of the sulphuric acid.

2LiOH

n = CV
n = 0.02 × 0.1
n = 0.002 moles

n (H_2SO_4) = 0.001

C = $\frac{n}{V}$

C = $\frac{0.001}{0.0185}$

C = 0.0054 moll^{-1}

_____ moll^{-1}

3. The main use for lithium carbonate is in antidepressant drugs for which a high purity is required. The purity of a sample of lithium carbonate can be checked by titration with sulfuric acid.

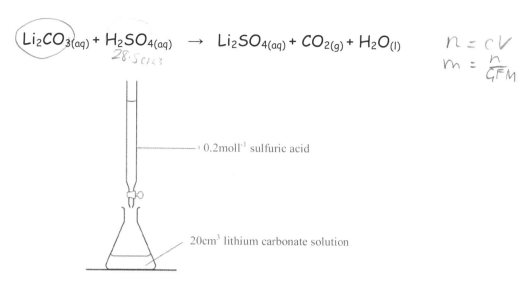

$Li_2CO_{3(aq)} + H_2SO_{4(aq)} \rightarrow Li_2SO_{4(aq)} + CO_{2(g)} + H_2O_{(l)}$
28.5cm3

$n = cV$
$m = \dfrac{n}{GFM}$

' 0.2moll⁻¹ sulfuric acid

20cm³ lithium carbonate solution

28.5cm³ of the sulfuric acid was required to exactly neutralise the lithium carbonate solution.
Calculate the concentration, in moll⁻¹, of the lithium carbonate solution.

_____ moll⁻¹

4. A pupil carried out a titration to find the concentration of a potassium hydroxide solution using 0.10moll⁻¹ hydrochloric acid.

$KOH_{(aq)} + HCl_{(aq)} \rightarrow KCl_{(aq)} + H_2O_{(l)}$

a. What must be added to the flask to show the end-point of the titration?

b. The average volume of hydrochloric acid needed to neutralise 20cm³ of the potassium hydroxide solution is 25cm³.
Calculate the concentration of the potassium hydroxide solution.

_____ moll⁻¹

5.   A sample of a pure dry salt can be made following a number of steps. Select the correct order of steps to make a dry sample of sodium sulfate.

A. Keep heating until 2/3 of the solution has evaporated	B. Stir until the sodium carbonate has all reacted	C. Add a spatula of sodium carbonate powder to the beaker
D. Continue to add spatulas of sodium carbonate until there is a layer of unreacted powder on the bottom.	E. Place the evaporating basin on a tripod & gauze and heat with a Bunsen burner.	F. Remove the evaporating basin and leave overnight for the crystals to form.
G. Pour the contents of the beaker into a filter funnel with filter paper	H. Pour 50cm^3 of 1.0moll^{-1} sulfuric acid into a beaker	I. Collect the filtrate in an evaporating basin

a.   Correct Order:

b.   An alternative method to make sodium sulfate is to titrate 50cm^3 of 1.0moll^{-1} sulfuric acid solution with a sodium hydroxide solution. In an experiment it was found that 50cm^3 of a sodium hydroxide solution completely neutralised the 50cm^3 of 1.0moll^{-1} sulfuric acid solution.

Calculate the concentration of the sodium hydroxide solution.

_____ moll^{-1}

Unit 2 — Homologous Series

HOMOLOGOUS SERIES

Family of compounds with the same general formula and similar chemical properties.

Alkanes: Saturated hydrocarbons containing just carbon-carbon single bonds.

Have a general formula C_nH_{2n+2}.

Most used as fuels.

Longer chains have higher melting & boiling points.

Alkenes: Unsaturated hydrocarbons containing a carbon-carbon double bond.

Test for unsaturation is the rapid decolourisation of bromine solution.

Have a general formula C_nH_{2n}.

Many used to make plastics.

Undergo **addition reactions** with H_2 to form alkanes and H_2O to form alcohols.

Cycloalkanes: Saturated hydrocarbons with a ring structure and carbon-carbon single bonds.

Have a general formula C_nH_{2n}.

NAMING HYDROCARBONS

A prefix is used to tell you the number of carbon atoms in the chain:

Number	prefix	Mnemonic
1	meth	**m**onkeys
2	eth	**e**at
3	prop	**p**eeled
4	but	**b**ananas
5	pent	**p**rivately
6	hex	**h**ating
7	hept	**h**airy
8	oct	**o**nes

STRUCTURAL FORMULAE

Full Structural Formulae:

Shows all the atoms and all the bonds.

e.g. propane   propene

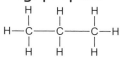

cyclopropane

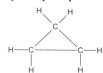

Shortened Structural Formulae:

Shows what is attached to each carbon atom without showing all the bonds.

e.g. propane   propene

$CH_3CH_2CH_3$ $CH_2=CHCH_3$

cyclopropane

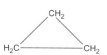

Molecular Formulae:

Shows the number of carbon, hydrogen and any other atoms in the molecule.

e.g. propane   propene

C_3H_8 C_3H_6

cyclopropane

C_3H_6

ISOMERS

Hydrocarbons with the same molecular formula but different structural formula are called **isomers**.

Alkanes can be converted into isomers through a process called catalytic reforming. The chain length is shortened and branches added.

e.g.

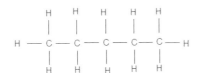

pentane - C_5H_{12} 2-methylbutane - C_5H_{12}

With alkenes changing the position of the double bond will also form isomers.

e.g.

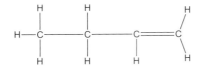

but-1-ene - C_4H_8 but-2-ene - C_4H_8

As alkenes and cycloalkanes have the same general formula, they are isomers of one another when they have the same number of carbon atoms.

e.g.

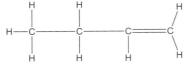 

but-1-ene - C_4H_8 cyclobutane - C_4H_8

SYSTEMATIC NAMING

Hydrocarbons are named using a systematic method.

Step 1   Identify the longest continuous chain of carbon atoms, including any double bond.

Step 2   Number the carbons atoms starting at the end carbon nearest the double bond or branch if there isn't a double bond.

Step 3   Identify the position of the double bond, if there is one.

Step 4   Identify the position of, number of and type of branches, if there is one carbon atom in a branch it is called methyl, if two ethyl. If there are 2 branches it's di-, if 3 branches tri-.

Step 5   Name the structure, starting with the branches, then the chain length and then the position of the double bond.

e.g.

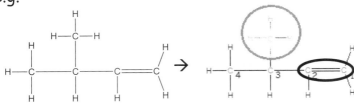 = 3-methyl but-1-ene

Prefixes

Complete the following table of prefixes found in hydrocarbon names and the number of carbons they represent. **Note they are not in numerical order.**

Prefix	**Oct-**		**Meth-**		**Pent-**		**Prop-**	
Number of carbon atoms		**6**		**2**		**7**		**4**

Drawing Hydrocarbons

Complete the following table of structures by identifying the correct letter that represents the structure that should be in the table.

A = 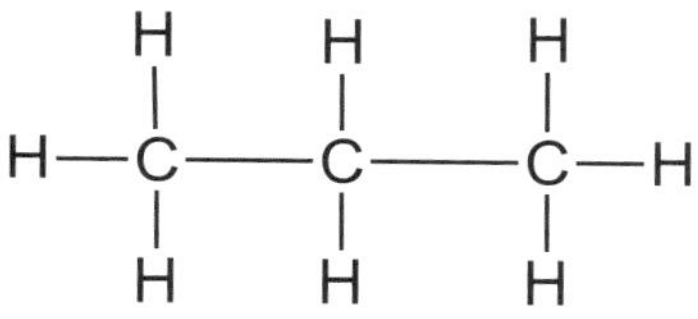

B = 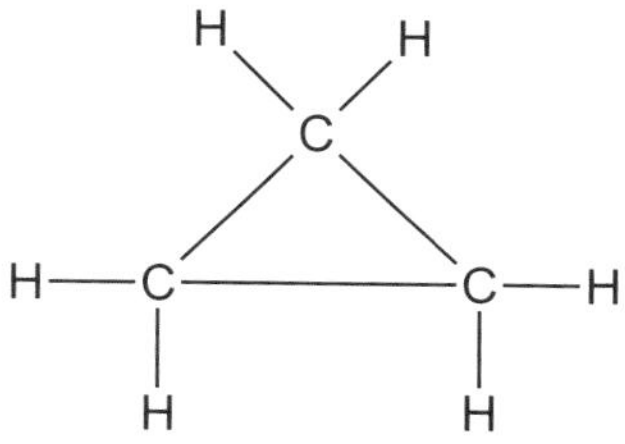

C = 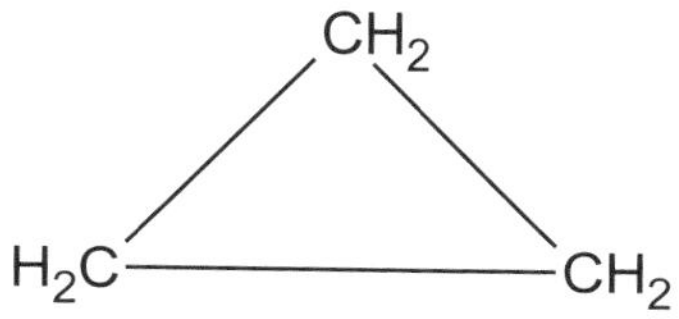

D = CH_2CHCH_3 E = C_3H_6 F = C_3H_8

Full Structural Formula	**Shortened Structural Formula**	**Molecular Formula**
		C_3H_6
	$CH_3CH_2CH_3$	
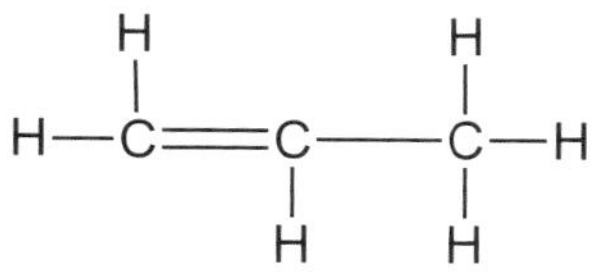		

General Formulae

General formulae show the ratio of hydrogens to carbons in hydrocarbons, some general formulae show the presence of other elements as well.
Connect the name or structure to the correct general formula. The first one has been done for you.

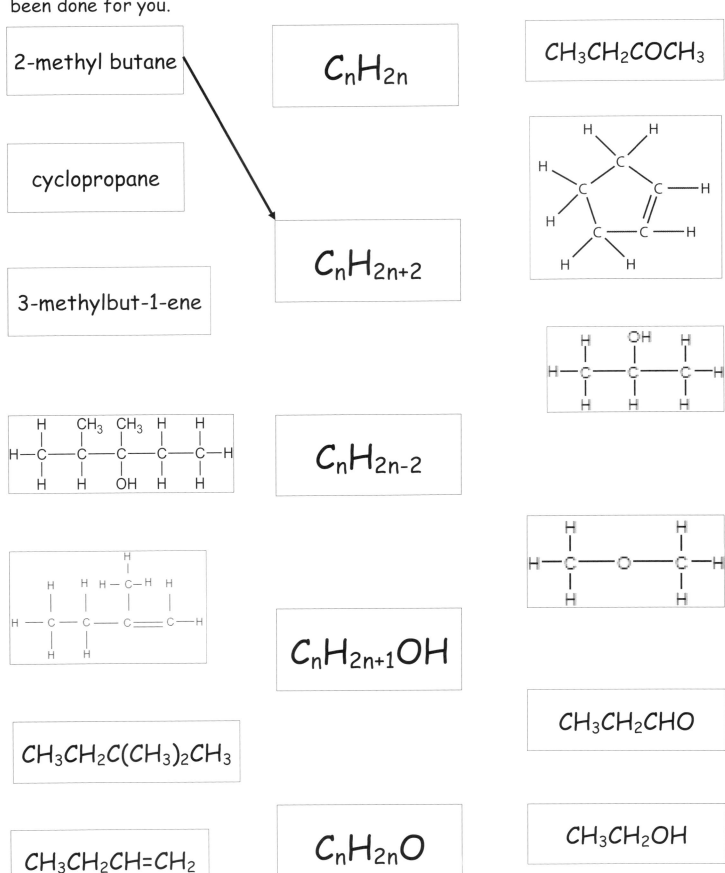

2-methyl butane

C_nH_{2n}

$CH_3CH_2COCH_3$

cyclopropane

C_nH_{2n+2}

3-methylbut-1-ene

C_nH_{2n-2}

$C_nH_{2n+1}OH$

$CH_3CH_2C(CH_3)_2CH_3$

CH_3CH_2CHO

$CH_3CH_2CH=CH_2$

$C_nH_{2n}O$

CH_3CH_2OH

Chemical Misconceptions

A student has completed a table showing the full structural formula, shortened structural formula and molecular formula of the first four members of the alkenes. They have made a number of mistakes, can you identify them and put the correct answer in the space below the table:

Alkene	Full Structural Formula	Shortened Structural Formula	Molecular Formula
ethane	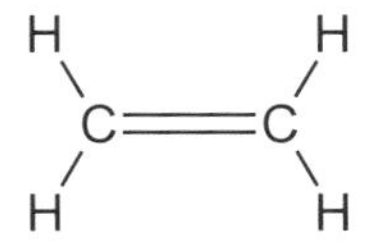	$CH_2{=}CH_2$	C_2H_4
propene	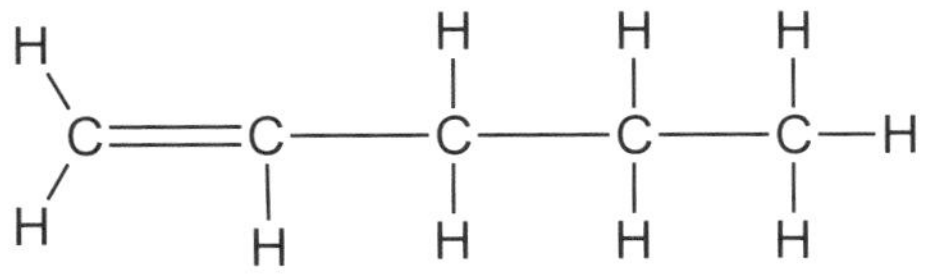	$CH_2{=}CHCH_3$	C3H6
butene	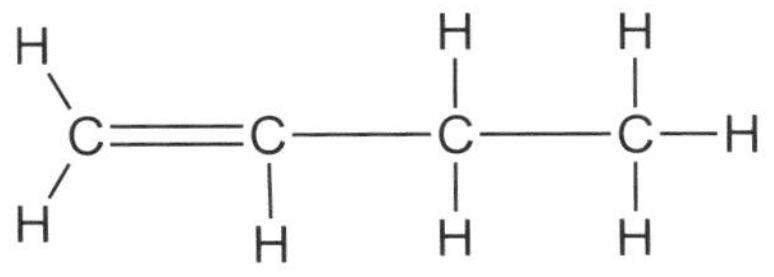	$CH_2{=}CH_2CH_2CH_3$	C_4H_8
pentene	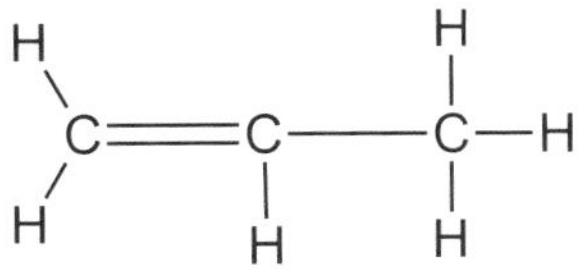	$CH_2{=}CHCH_2CH_2CH_3$	C_5H_{12}

1.

2.

3.

4.

5.

6.

Systematic Naming

Identify the correct systematic name for the following hydrocarbon compounds. The first one has been done for you.

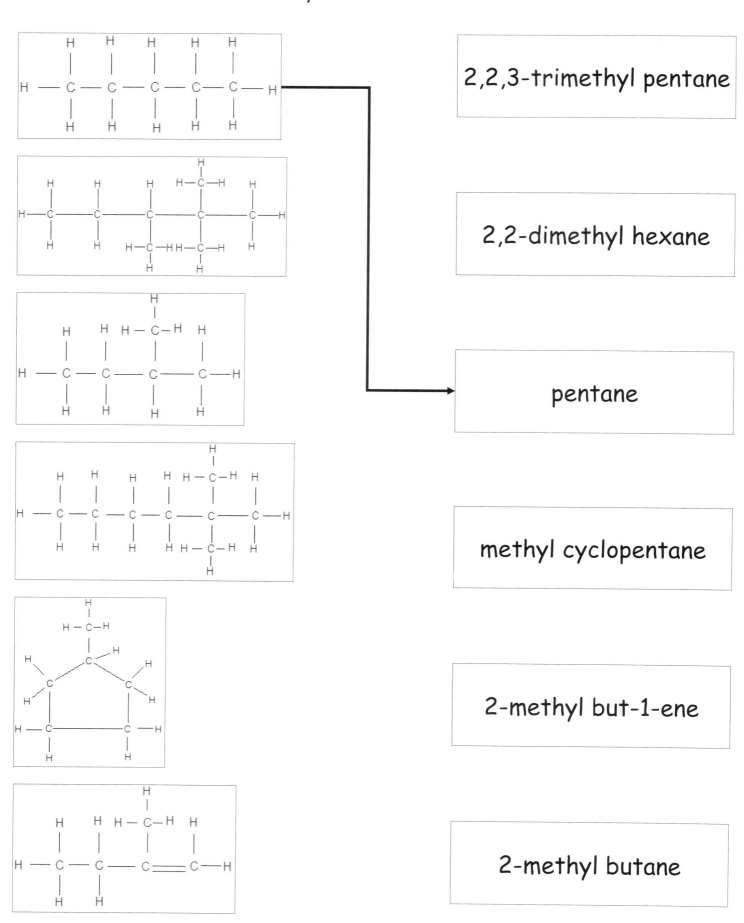

Isomers

Draw a line connecting the isomer pairs. The first one has been done for you.

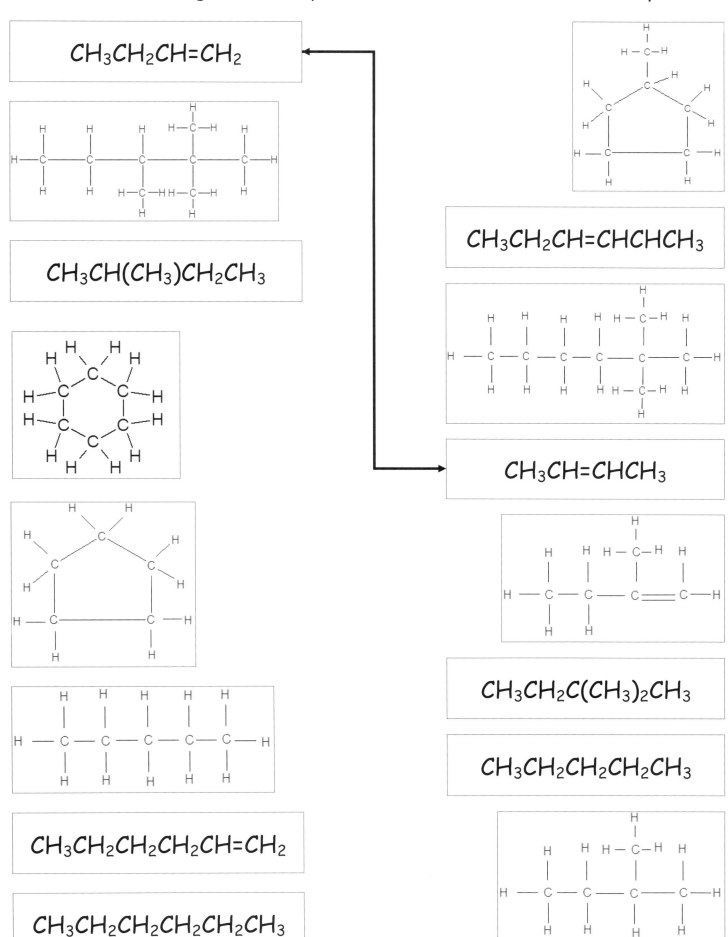

$CH_3CH_2CH=CH_2$

$CH_3CH(CH_3)CH_2CH_3$

$CH_3CH_2CH=CHCHCH_3$

$CH_3CH=CHCH_3$

$CH_3CH_2C(CH_3)_2CH_3$

$CH_3CH_2CH_2CH_2CH_3$

$CH_3CH_2CH_2CH_2CH=CH_2$

$CH_3CH_2CH_2CH_2CH_2CH_3$

Quiz Word

Answer the following questions to complete the quiz word and then try and work out what the key phrase in the **bold** boxes should be.

1. Alkenes and cycloalkanes with the same molecular formula are this. (7)
2. Saturated hydrocarbons with a ring structure are called this. (12)
3. All alkenes contain one of these bonds. (6)
4. Isomers have different structures but their molecular formulas are this. (4)
5. Alkenes are often described as being this. (11)
6. This type of structural formula only shows what is attached to each carbon atom and not the bonds. (9)

Practice Questions

1. Alkylation is a method used in the petrochemical industry to make branched chain alkanes as additives to petrol.

$$CH_3-\underset{\underset{CH_3}{|}}{\overset{\overset{CH_3}{|}}{C}}-H + CH_2=\underset{CH_3}{\overset{CH_3}{C}} \longrightarrow CH_3-\underset{\underset{CH_3}{|}}{\overset{\overset{CH_3}{|}}{C}}-CH_2-\underset{\underset{H}{|}}{\overset{\overset{CH_3}{|}}{C}}-CH_3$$

ai.   In the above example give the systematic name for the product.

ii.   Name the type of chemical reaction shown above.

b.   Draw the product of the following reaction.

$$H_3C-\underset{\underset{CH_3}{|}}{\overset{\overset{CH_3}{|}}{C}}-CH_3 + H_2C=\underset{CH_3}{\overset{CH_3}{C}} \longrightarrow$$

2.   Propane can be made using the Wurtz Process as shown below:

$$H-\underset{\underset{H}{|}}{\overset{\overset{H}{|}}{C}}-\underset{\underset{H}{|}}{\overset{\overset{H}{|}}{C}}-I \quad I-\underset{\underset{H}{|}}{\overset{\overset{H}{|}}{C}}-H \xrightarrow{2Na} H-\underset{\underset{H}{|}}{\overset{\overset{H}{|}}{C}}-\underset{\underset{H}{|}}{\overset{\overset{H}{|}}{C}}-\underset{\underset{H}{|}}{\overset{\overset{H}{|}}{C}}-H \quad + 2NaI$$

Draw the structural formulae of two reactants that could be used to make pentane.

3. Mercaptans are a homologous series of smelly compounds that are often used to make natural gas more easily detected by smell when there is a gas leak.

The table below gives the first four members of this group.

Name	Shortened Structural Formula	Chemical Formula
methyl mercaptan	CH_3SH	CH_4S
ethyl mercaptan	CH_3CH_2SH	C_2H_6S
propyl mercaptan	$CH_3CH_2CH_2SH$	C_3H_8S
butyl mercaptan	$CH_3CH_2CH_2CH_2SH$	$C_4H_{10}S$

a. What is the general formula of this homologous series.

b. Draw the shortened structural formula of pentyl mercaptan.

c. Draw the full structural formula of an isomer of butyl mercaptan.

4. Markovnikov's rule states that during the addition reaction of an alkene with a hydrogen halide, the hydrogen atom will always join to the carbon atom, with the double bond, with the most hydrogen atoms directly bonded to it.

a. Draw the full structural formula of the product of the addition reaction between but-1-ene and hydrogen bromide.

b. **Name** the alkene that would be used to create the following molecule:

c. Draw the full structural formula of an isomer of but-1-ene.

EVERYDAY CONSUMER PRODUCTS

Families of hydrocarbons with important functional groups. Found in a range of everyday household items.

Alcohols: Hydrocarbons with a hydroxyl functional group (-OH) and names ending in -ol. Used as solvents and fuels as they burn with a clean flame. Also used to make other compounds including esters.

Carboxylic Acids: Hydrocarbons with a carboxyl functional group (-COOH) and names ending in -anoic acid. Used as solvents, preservatives in the food industry and cleaning products to remove limescale. Also used to make other compounds including esters.

Esters: Formed from the reaction between an alcohol and carboxylic acid. They contain the ester link (-COO- or -OCO-) also known as alkyl alkanoates. Used as solvents, flavourings & fragrances (due to their sweet smell) and in some plastics.

SYSTEMATIC NAMING

Branched alcohols are named in the same way as alkenes.
Name the structure, starting with the branches, then the chain length and then the position of the hydroxyl group.

e.g.

2-methyl butan-1-ol

Branched carboxylic acids are named in the same way as alkanes.
Name the structure, starting with the branches, then the chain length and then the -anoic acid ending.

e.g.

$$CH_3CHCH_2COOH$$
$$|$$
$$CH_3$$

2-methyl butanoic acid

FUNCTIONAL GROUP STRUCTURES

Functional Group	Full Structural Formula	Shortened Structural Formula	Molecular Formula
Hydroxyl (alcohols) e.g. ethanol		CH_3CH_2OH	C_2H_5OH
Carboxyl (carboxylic acids) e.g. ethanoic acid		CH_3COOH	CH_3CO_2H
Ester link (esters) e.g. methyl propananoate		$CH_3CH_2COOCH_3$	$C_2H_5CO_2CH_3$

ENERGY FROM FUELS

A fuel is a substance that burns to produce energy.

Both alkanes and alcohols are used as fuels as they are very flammable and release a lot of heat during combustion.

All combustion reactions are exothermic and the energy released by a fuel can be calculated using the following experiment and calculation:

$E_h = cm\Delta T$ where E_h = energy released by the fuel

$\quad\quad\quad\quad\quad\quad\quad$ c = specific heat capacity of water

$\quad\quad\quad\quad\quad\quad\quad\quad$ = $4.18 kJkg^{-1}\,°C^{-1}$

$\quad\quad\quad\quad\quad\quad\quad$ m = mass of water in can in kg ($1cm^3$ = 0.001kg)

$\quad\quad\quad\quad\quad\quad\quad$ ΔT = change in temperature of water

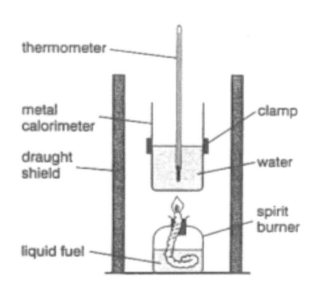

Set up the apparatus as shown recording the volume of water in the metal calorimeter or beaker. Take the temperature of the water before and after combustion. The water will absorb the heat and this can be calculated by using the above equation (found on p3 of your data booklet):

The value calculated for E_h is often lower than expected due to incomplete combustion and heat loss to the surroundings.

BALANCED EQUATIONS

When a substance is combusted, the reaction can be represented using a balanced chemical equation (see p42 of this book) :

e.g. $\quad$ C₂H₅OH $\quad\quad$ + $\quad$ 3O₂ $\quad\quad$ → $\quad\quad$ 2CO₂ $\quad$ + $\quad$ 3H₂O

$\quad\quad\quad\quad\quad$ C=2 $\quad\quad\quad\quad\quad\quad\quad\quad\quad\quad\quad\quad\quad\quad$ C=1̶ =2

$\quad\quad\quad\quad\quad$ H=6 $\quad\quad\quad\quad\quad\quad\quad\quad\quad\quad\quad\quad\quad\quad$ H=2̶ =6

$\quad\quad\quad\quad\quad$ O=3̶ =7 $\quad\quad\quad\quad\quad\quad\quad\quad\quad\quad\quad\quad$ O=2̶ =5=7

becomes $\quad\quad$ **C₂H₅OH** $\quad\quad$ + $\quad$ **3O₂** $\quad\quad$ → $\quad\quad$ **2CO₂** $\quad$ + $\quad\quad\quad$ **3H₂O**

The quantities of reactants needed or products produced can be calculated using mole calculations as shown on p43 of this book.

Chemical Misconceptions

A student has completed a table showing the full structural formula, shortened structural formula and molecular formula of the first four members of the alcohols. They have made a number of mistakes, can you identify them and put the correct answer in the space below the table:

Alkanol	Full Structural Formula	Shortened Structural Formula	Molecular Formula
methanol		CH_3OH	CH_3O
ethanol		CH_3CH_3O	C_2H_5OH
pentanol		$CH_3CH_2CH_2OH$	$C3H_7OH$
butanol		$CH_3CH_2\ CH_2CH_2CHOH$	C_4H_9OH

1.

2.

3.

4.

5.

6.

Systematic Naming

Match the following alcohol compounds to the correct systematic name. The first one has been done for you.

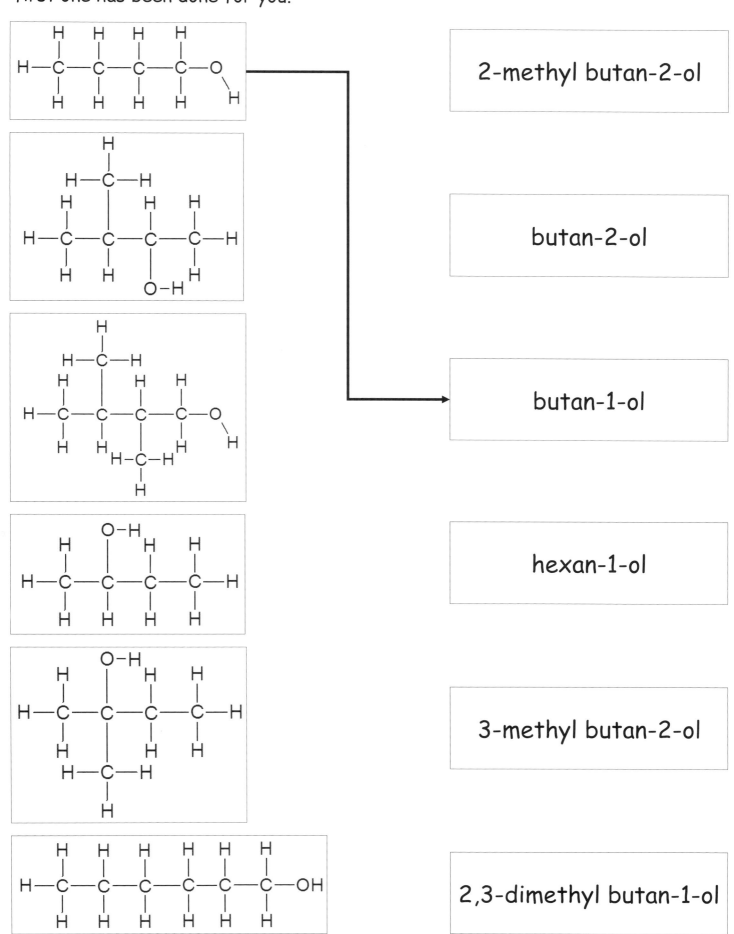

2-methyl butan-2-ol

butan-2-ol

butan-1-ol

hexan-1-ol

3-methyl butan-2-ol

2,3-dimethyl butan-1-ol

Carboxylic acid

A student has partially completed a table showing the names and structures of the first four carboxylic acids. Complete the table by adding the correct letter to represent the name or structure shown below:

A pentanoic acid   **B** propanoic acid   **C** methanoic acid

D   **E** 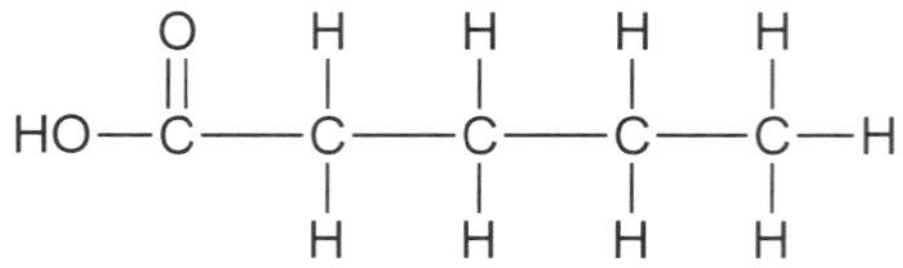   **F**

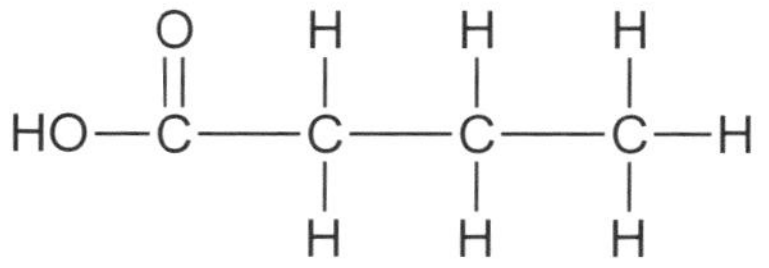

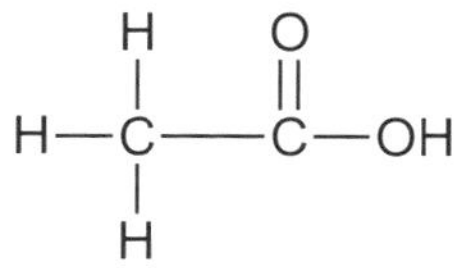

G $CH_3CH_2CH_2COOH$ **H** $CH_3CH_2CH_2CH_2COOH$ **I** HCOOH

J C_2H_5COOH **K** C_3H_7COOH **L** CH_3COOH

Alkanoic acid	Full Structural Formula	Shortened Structural Formula	Molecular Formula
	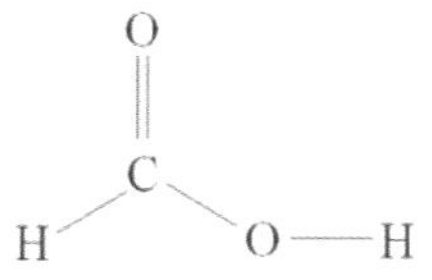		HCOOH
ethanoic acid		CH_3COOH	
	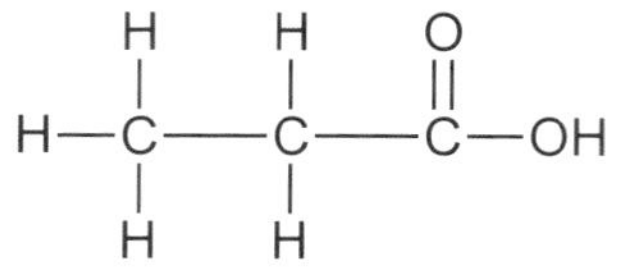	CH_3CH_2COOH	
butanoic acid			C_3H_7COOH

Chemical Misconceptions

A student has completed a set of notes on everyday chemicals, however they have made a number of mistakes. Can you identify them and write the correct note in the space below:

Alcohols are made by distillation from various sources of sugar. Fermentation is used to purify the alcohol. Alcohol is used as a fuel because it doesn't burn well and produces less pollution. They are also good solvents.

Carboxylic acids have many uses in the food and drinks industry to give a sweet taste. Vinegar is butanoic acid and is used as a preservative and to remove limescale. Carboxylic acids are not used as solvents.

Esters are made by reacting carboxylic acids with alkanes. They are foul smelling and so get used in flavourings. They are good solvents and are also found in all plastics.

_____

_____

_____

_____

_____

_____

_____

_____

_____

_____

Identifying Esters

Put a tick next to all the substances that are esters or contain an ester link.

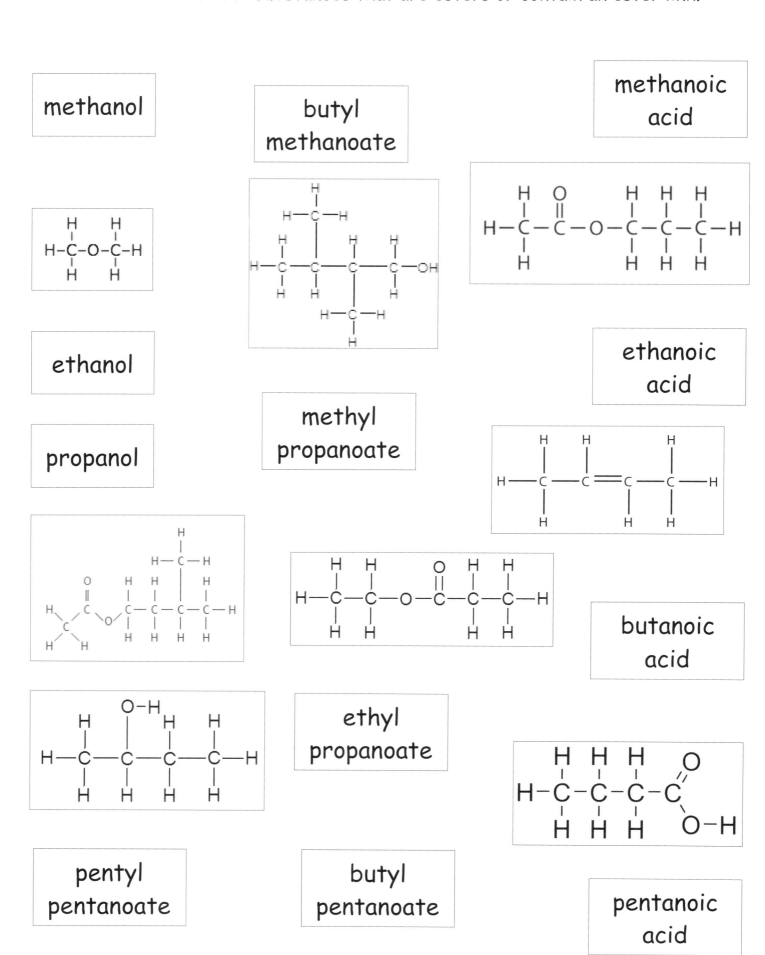

methanol

butyl methanoate

methanoic acid

ethanol

methyl propanoate

ethanoic acid

propanol

butanoic acid

ethyl propanoate

pentyl pentanoate

butyl pentanoate

pentanoic acid

Functional Groups

Look at the chemical compounds' names or structures A to Q and decide which group it belongs to; give the name of its functional group, then write the letter in the correct box. The first two have been done for you.

Group	Functional Group	Name or Structure
alkenes		
cycloalkanes	ring	A,
alcohols		
carboxylic acids		
esters	ester link	B,

A   cyclopropane

B   ethyl propanoate

C   pentan-2-ol

D   methanoic acid

E   2-methyl pent-1-ene

F   methyl cyclobutane

G $CH_3CH_2CH=CH_2$

H $CH_3CH_2CH_2OH$

I $CH_3CH_2CH_2OCOCH_3$

J $CH_3CH_2CH_2COOH$

K   HCOOH

L $CH_3CH_2CH(OH)CH_3$

M

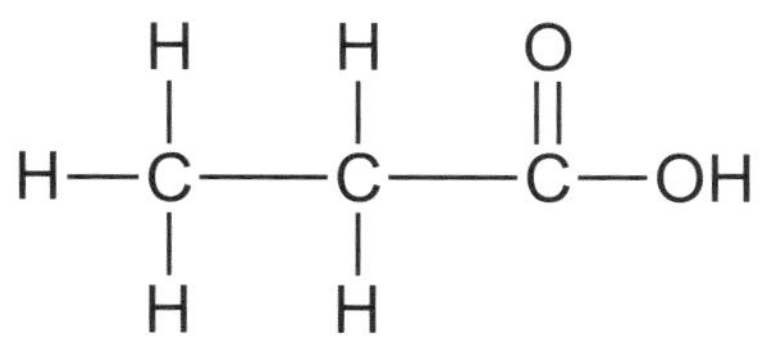

N

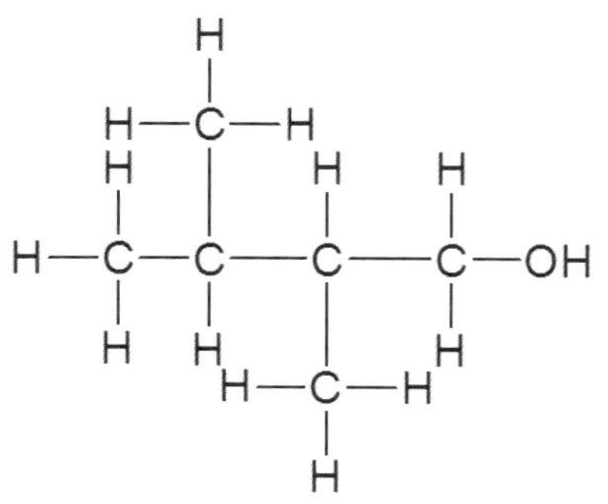

O

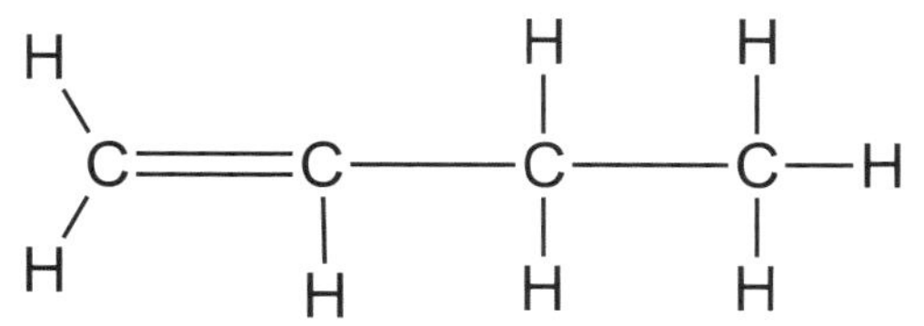

P

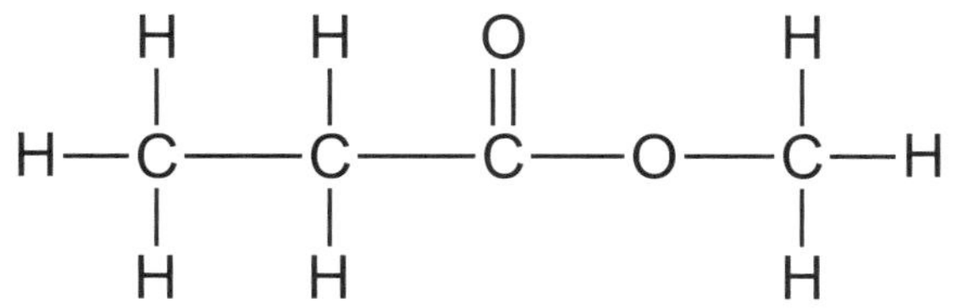

Q

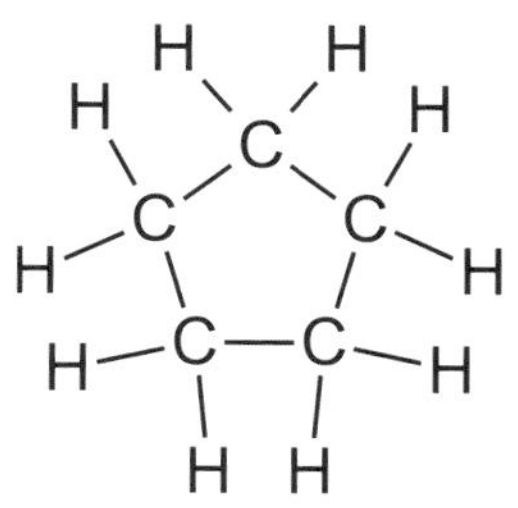

Quiz Word

Answer the following questions to complete the quiz word and then try and work out what the key phrase in the **bold** boxes should be.

1. Functional group found in carboxylic acids. (8)
2. One of the things esters are used for. (11)
3. Functional group found in alcohols. (8)
4. Alcohols, carboxylic acids and esters all get used as this. (8)
5. Hydrocarbons with very long chains with repeating ester links are found as these. (8)
6. All esters contain one of these. (5,4)

Design an Experiment

Using **any** of the pieces of equipment and other information given below, describe how you could work out how much energy each fuel releases when burnt, making sure that it is a fair test. You may draw a diagram to help:

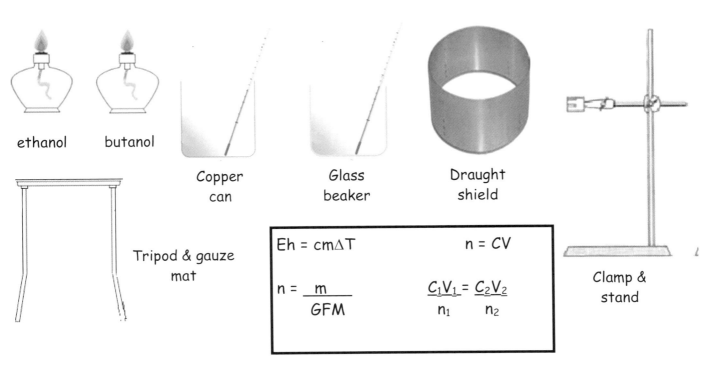

ethanol   butanol

Copper
can

Glass
beaker

Draught
shield

Tripod & gauze
mat

Clamp &
stand

$$Eh = cm\Delta T \qquad\qquad n = CV$$

$$n = \dfrac{m}{GFM} \qquad\qquad \dfrac{C_1V_1}{n_1} = \dfrac{C_2V_2}{n_2}$$

Practice Questions

1. The beech bark beetle will use a group of chemicals called pheromones in order to attract a mate. One of the components of this pheromone contains an ester link and another functional group and is shown below:

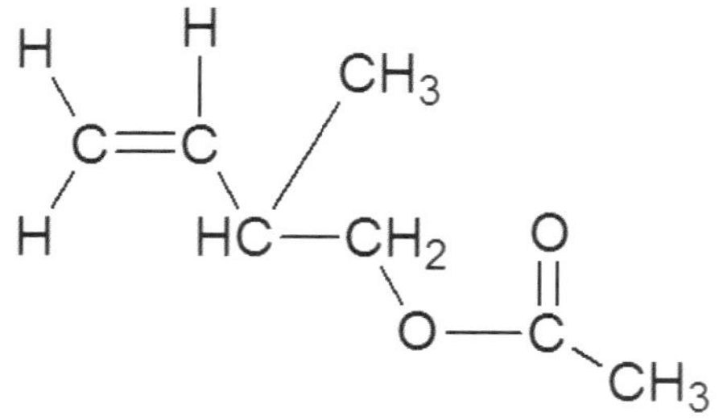

a. Identify the other functional group.

b. Scientists have tried to recreate this molecule in the lab using the following alcohol:

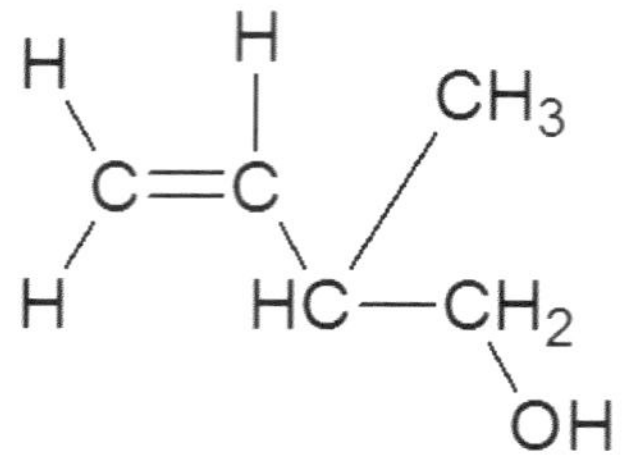

i. Draw the full structural formula of the carboxylic acid that they would need to use in order to create the beech bark beetle pheromone component.

ii. Give another use of carboxylic acids other than for making esters.

c. The full structural formulae for the first three members of the carboxylic acid family are shown.

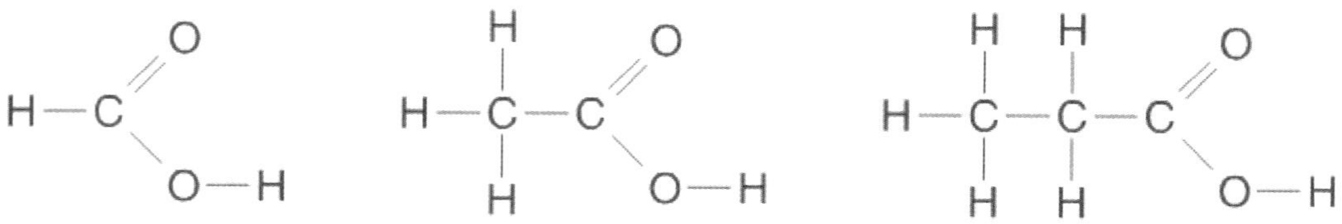

Methanoic acid   Ethanoic acid   Propanoic acid

Suggest a general formula for this homologous series.

2. Many fragrances are due to the presence of esters. The table below shows some common smells attributed to esters and the alcohol and carboxylic acid that form them.

Ester	Smells like	Alcohol	Carboxylic acid
ethyl butanoate	pineapple	ethanol	butanoic acid
propyl ethanoate	pears	A	ethanoic acid
B	apples	methanol	butanoic acid
octyl ethanoate	oranges	octanol	C

a. Identify the names of the chemicals A, B and C.

b. Propyl ethanoate is shown below and is also used as a solvent in many glues.
   Circle the ester link.

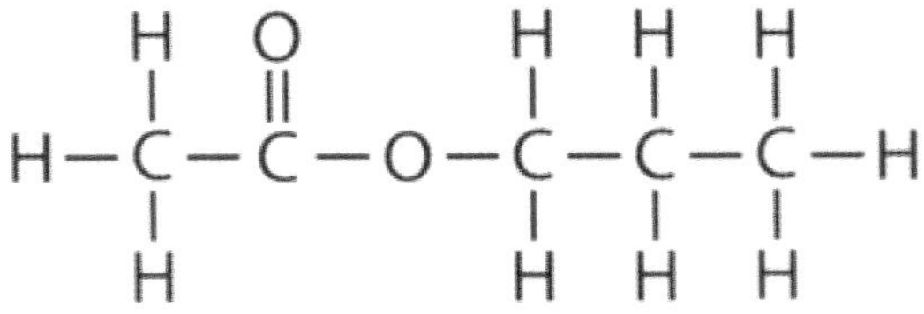

3. Cocoa leaves have been chewed by South American indigenous people for pain relief for centuries. The drug cocaine was found to be present in the leaves and this was the main chemical causing the pain relief. The structure of cocaine is shown below:

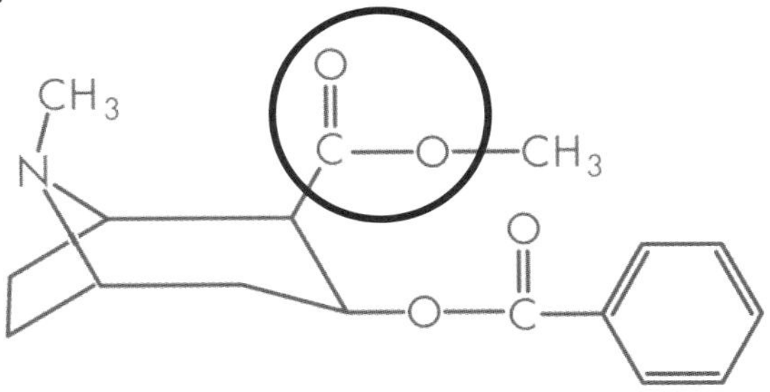

a. Identify the group of atoms circled in the above structure.

b. As our bodies metabolise cocaine it breaks down through the process of hydrolysis. One of these products is benzoic acid. What group of compounds does benzoic acid belong to?

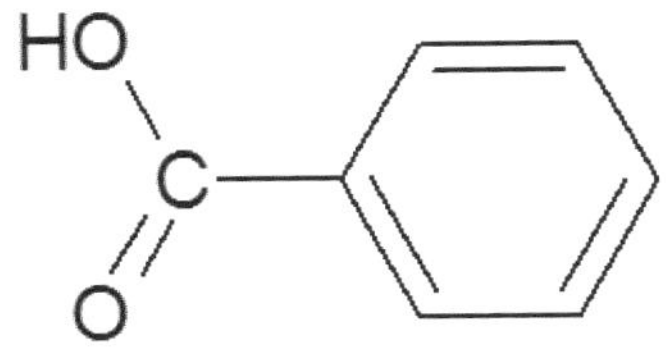

4. Lactones are a group of compounds that have an important role in some fruit flavours and as industrial solvents. Butyrolactone is a lactone found in paint stripper and is formed in the following reaction;

CH$_2$—OH
H$_2$C
CH$_2$—C—OH
            O

⟶

CH$_2$
H$_2$C   O
CH$_2$—C
              O

a. Caprolactone is made from the following molecule, draw the structural formula for the caprolactone.

CH$_2$—CH$_2$
H$_2$C   OH
H$_2$C
     CH$_2$—C—OH
              ‖
              O

⟶

b. The molecules used to make lactones are called hydroxy acids. Give the names of the two functional groups found in hydroxy acids

5. The energy released by burning 1g of rocket fuel can be determined from measurements using the apparatus shown.

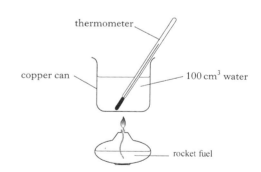

In an experiment, the following results were obtained.

Volume of water 100cm^3, temperature at the start 20^{0}C and temperature of water after 0.1g of rocket fuel had been burnt, 80^{0}C.

Use these results to calculate the energy released per gram, kJ g^{-1} of rocket fuel.
Show your working clearly.

_____kJg^{-1}

Unit 3 Metals

METALLIC BONDING

The outer (valence) electrons in a metal are weakly held, so they are free to move. This leaves positive metal ions surrounded by a sea of delocalised electrons. The attraction the electrons have for the positive nuclei holds the atoms together.

Generally metallic bonds are strong but with a large range of values and hence different melting points, depending on the size of the atom and number of outer electrons.

The ability of the delocalised electrons to move around allows metals to conduct electricity.

Metals are insoluble in water but some react violently forming alkalis.

% METAL IN ORES

If the chemical formula of the ore is known the percentage of the metal in the ore can be calculated.

E.g.   To work out %mass of iron in iron(III) oxide.

Step 1   Calculate the GFM of the ore Fe_2O_3

3×16
$\underline{2 \times 56}$
$160g$

Step 2   Calculate total mass of metal in the formula = $2 \times 56 = 112g$

Step 3   Divide the total mass of metal by the GFM and multiply by 100.

%Fe in Fe_2O_3 $= 112/160 \times 100$
$= \underline{70\%}$

REACTIVITY SERIES

Metals can be placed in an order of reactivity, depending on how violently they react with water, acids and oxygen. The most reactive metals at the top, the least at the bottom.

potassium   MOST
sodium
lithium
calcium
magnesium
aluminium
zinc
iron
tin
copper
silver   LEAST

EXTRACTING METALS

The more reactive a metal is, the harder it is to extract it from its ore (metal oxide).

Heat Alone - Only works for the least reactive metals like silver.

$2(Ag^+)_2O^{2-}_{(s)} \rightarrow 4Ag_{(s)} + O_{2(g)}$

Heat & Reducing Agent (C, CO, CH_4 or H_2, remove the oxygen from the metal oxide) - Copper to iron

$Cu^{2+}O^{2-}_{(s)} + CO_{(g)} \rightarrow Cu_{(s)} + CO_{2(g)}$

Electrolysis of melt - Zinc and above

$2Mg^{2+}O^{2-}_{(l)} \rightarrow 2Mg_{(l)} + O_{2(g)}$

IONIC EQUATIONS

The reactions of metals can be shown using balanced ionic equations. These only show those substances, whether they are atoms or ions, that are actually involved in the reaction. All other ions are called **spectator ions** and are not shown.

Reaction of metals with water - sodium with water

$$2Na_{(s)} + 2H_2O_{(l)} \rightarrow 2NaOH_{(aq)} + H_{2(g)}$$
$$2Na_{(s)} + 2H_2O_{(l)} \rightarrow 2Na^+_{(aq)} + 2OH^-_{(aq)} + H_{2(g)}$$

Reaction of metals with acid - magnesium with hydrochloric acid

$$Mg_{(s)} + 2HCl_{(aq)} \rightarrow MgCl_{2(aq)} + H_{2(g)}$$
$$Mg_{(s)} + 2H^+_{(aq)} + \cancel{2Cl^-_{(aq)}} \rightarrow Mg^{2+}_{(aq)} + \cancel{2Cl^-_{(aq)}} + H_{2(g)}$$
$$Mg_{(s)} + 2H^+_{(aq)} \rightarrow Mg^{2+}_{(aq)} + H_{2(g)}$$

Reaction of metals with metal compounds - iron with copper sulfate

$$Fe_{(s)} + CuSO_{4(aq)} \rightarrow FeSO_{4(aq)} + Cu_{(s)}$$
$$Fe_{(s)} + Cu^{2+}_{(aq)} + \cancel{SO_4^{2-}_{(aq)}} \rightarrow Fe^{2+}_{(aq)} + Cu_{(s)} + \cancel{SO_4^{2-}_{(aq)}}$$
$$Fe_{(s)} + Cu^{2+}_{(aq)} \rightarrow Fe^{2+}_{(aq)} + Cu_{(s)}$$

REDOX REACTIONS

Reactions of metals often involve the transfer of electrons. When a substance loses electrons it's called oxidation; when a substance gains electrons it's called reduction (OILRIG). During a redox reaction both processes take place.

Ion-electron $\frac{1}{2}$ equations can show these processes.

e.g.

$$Fe_{(s)} + CuSO_{4(aq)} \rightarrow FeSO_{4(aq)} + Cu_{(s)}$$

The iron is being oxidized

$$Fe_{(s)} \rightarrow Fe^{2+}_{(aq)} + 2e^-$$

The copper ions are being reduced

$$Cu^{2+}_{(aq)} + 2e^- \rightarrow Cu_{(s)}$$

Combining the equations gives us the redox equation, note the electrons get cancelled out:

$$Fe_{(s)} + Cu^{2+}_{(aq)} \rightarrow Fe^{2+}_{(aq)} + Cu_{(s)}$$

ELECTROCHEMICAL CELLS

During redox reactions electrons flow from one substance to another, if these electrons are made to flow through wires an electrochemical cell is formed.

Zn electrode — Cu electrode
$ZnSO_{4(aq)}$ — $CuSO_{4(aq)}$

In the above cell, electrons flow from the zinc electrode to the copper, as metals higher up in the electrochemical series (p10 of the data booklet) will always donate electrons to those lower down. The salt bridge contains an electrolyte that completes the circuit.

The bigger the difference in their position in the electrochemical series the larger the voltage.

Its possible for non-metal electrodes to be used (e.g. carbon) as long as a redox reaction occurs at the electrodes. Fuel cells and rechargeable batteries utilise this.

Chemical Misconceptions

A teacher has marked a student's jotter but has not completed any corrections, identify what the students mistakes were and write the correct version in the space below:

Metallic bonding occurs in metal compounds. The outermost electrons are free to move and so form a sea of localised electrons surrounding negative metal ions. The pull of the sea of electrons for the metal ions holds the metal together.

Metals can have a range of melting points from very high to quite low as metallic bonds are weak. Their strength depends upon the size of the metal atoms and the number of outer electrons.

Metals cannot conduct electricity due to their delocalised electrons. Metals are very soluble in water and all react violently with water forming acidic solutions.

Very reactive metals will react with cold water, dilute acid but not oxygen. Unreactive metals often react with oxygen and acids.

The reactivity series is similar to the electrochemical series metals higher up are less reactive than those lower down.

_____

_____

_____

_____

_____

_____

_____

_____

Ionic Equations

Use the box of formulae below to help write out balanced ionic equations for the following reactions, making sure you remove any spectator ions.

$$K_{(s)} \quad Mg^{2+}_{(aq)} \quad Na_{(s)} \quad Na^+_{(aq)} \quad Zn_{(s)} \quad K^+_{(aq)} \quad Mg_{(s)} \quad Zn^{2+}_{(aq)} \quad H^+_{(aq)}$$

$$Cu_{(s)} \quad H_2O_{(l)} \quad H_{2(g)} \quad Cl^-_{(aq)} \quad O_{2(g)} \quad SO_4{}^{2-}_{(aq)} \quad OH^-_{(aq)} \quad Cu^{2+}O^{2-}_{(s)}$$

A. potassium + water → potassium hydroxide + hydrogen

B. zinc + hydrochloric acid → zinc(II) chloride + hydrogen

C. copper + oxygen → copper(II) oxide

D. sodium + water → sodium hydroxide + hydrogen

E. magnesium + sulfuric acid → magnesium sulfate + hydrogen

Extracting Metals

Depending on how reactive a metal is, different methods need to be used to extract them from their ore.

Connect the correct method for extracting each metal from its oxide. The first one has been done for you.

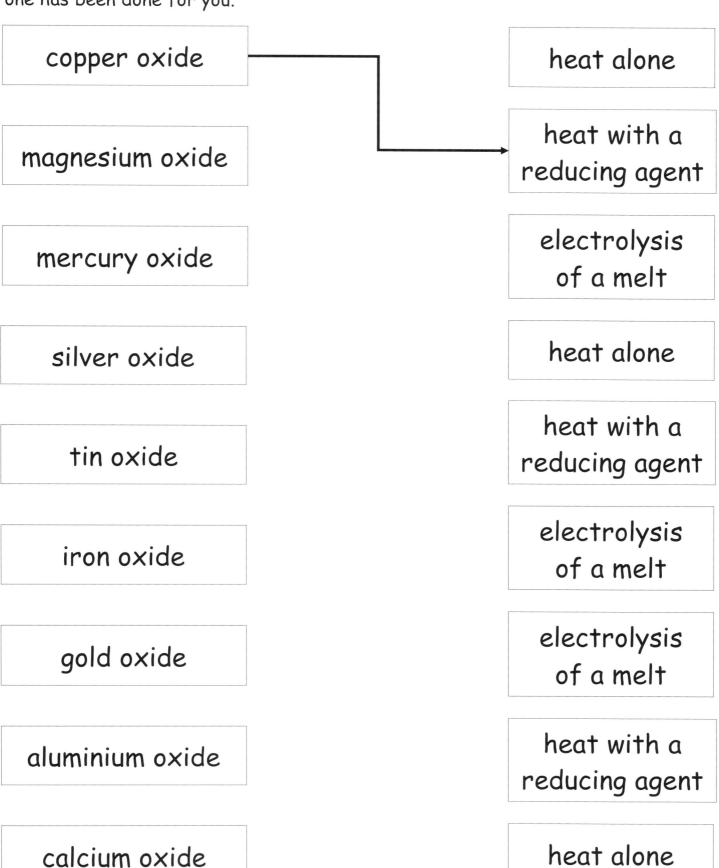

copper oxide	heat alone
magnesium oxide	heat with a reducing agent
mercury oxide	electrolysis of a melt
silver oxide	heat alone
tin oxide	heat with a reducing agent
iron oxide	electrolysis of a melt
gold oxide	electrolysis of a melt
aluminium oxide	heat with a reducing agent
calcium oxide	heat alone

Reducing Agents

Circle the reducing agent in each of the following chemical reactions. The first one has been done for you.

$Fe_2O_{3(s)}$ + $\boxed{3CO_{(g)}}$ → $2Fe_{(s)}$ + $3CO_{2(g)}$

$CuO_{(s)}$ + $H_{2(g)}$ → $H_2O_{(g)}$ + $Cu_{(s)}$

$C_{(s)}$ + $2SnO_{(s)}$ → $CO_{2(g)}$ + $2Sn_{(s)}$

$CH_{4(g)}$ + $4CuO_{(s)}$ → $4Cu_{(s)}$ + $CO_{2(g)}$ + $2H_2O_{(l)}$

$2FeO_{(s)}$ + $C_{(s)}$ → $2Fe_{(s)}$ + $CO_{2(g)}$

$TiCl_{4(l)}$ + $2Mg_{(s)}$ → $Ti_{(s)}$ + $2MgCl_{2(s)}$

$2Al_{(s)}$ + $Fe_2O_{3(s)}$ → $2Fe_{(s)}$ + $Al_2O_{3(s)}$

% Composition

Link the % mass of a metal to its compound. The first one has been done for you.

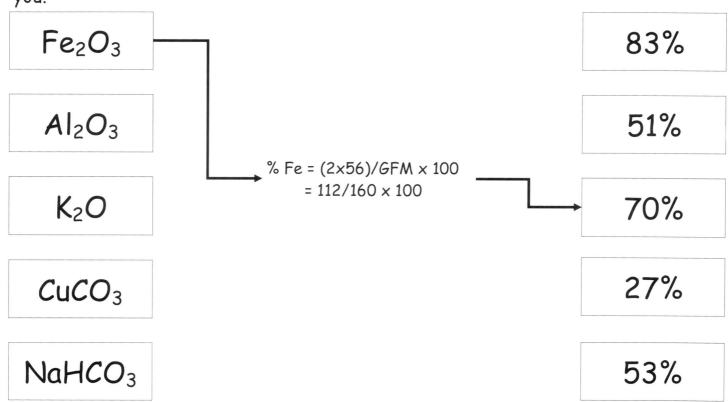

Fe_2O_3

Al_2O_3

K_2O

$CuCO_3$

$NaHCO_3$

% Fe = (2x56)/GFM x 100
    = 112/160 x 100

83%

51%

70%

27%

53%

Electrochemical Cells (I)

Look at the following electrochemical cells labelled A-F. Using the electrochemical series on p10 of your data booklet, decide which direction the electrical current will flow. Then draw an arrow above the meter to show the direction. The first one has been done for you.

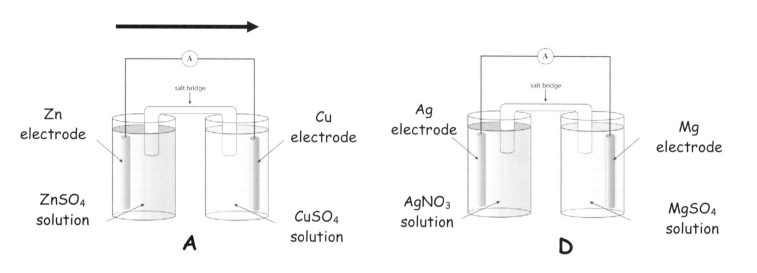

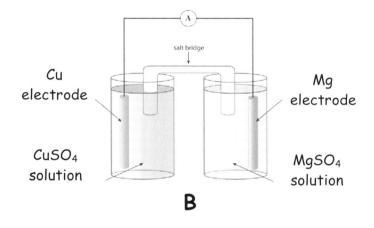

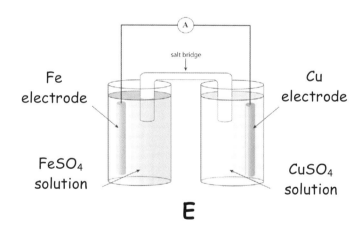

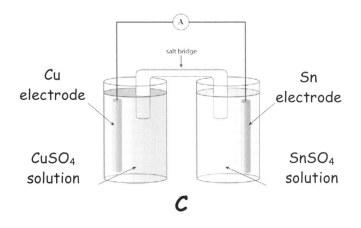

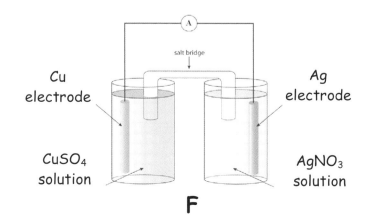

Electrochemical Cells (II)

Look at the following electrochemical cells labelled A-F. Using the electrochemical series on p10 of your data booklet, work out the order of the size of voltage they would produce. Put the letter of the cell with the highest voltage in the right hand box and the cell with the lowest voltage in the left hand box:

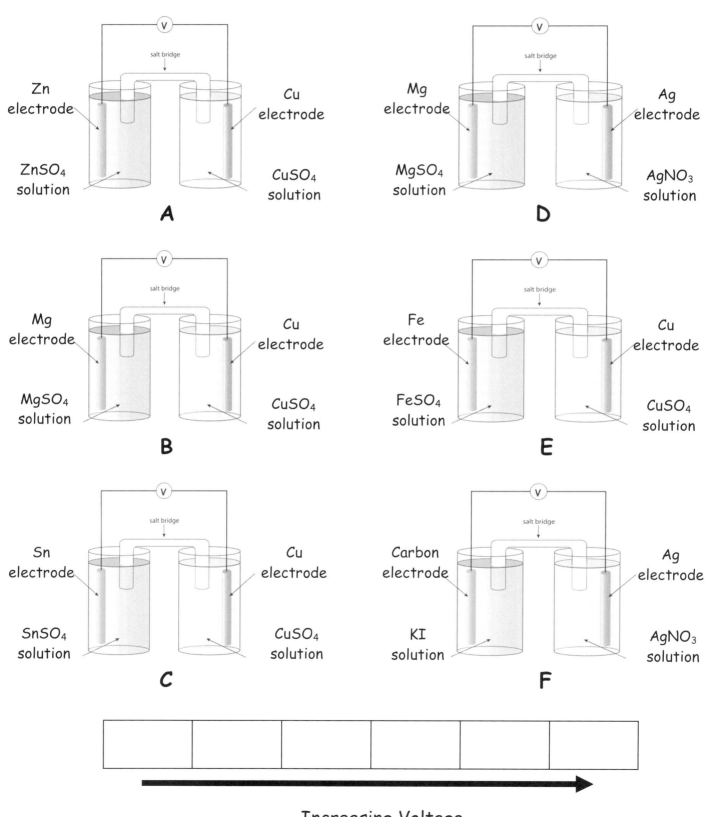

Increasing Voltage

Redox Equations

Combining oxidation and reduction ion-electron $\frac{1}{2}$ equations produces a redox equation.

Connect the correct oxidation and reduction $\frac{1}{2}$ equations to produce the given redox equation. The first has been done for you.

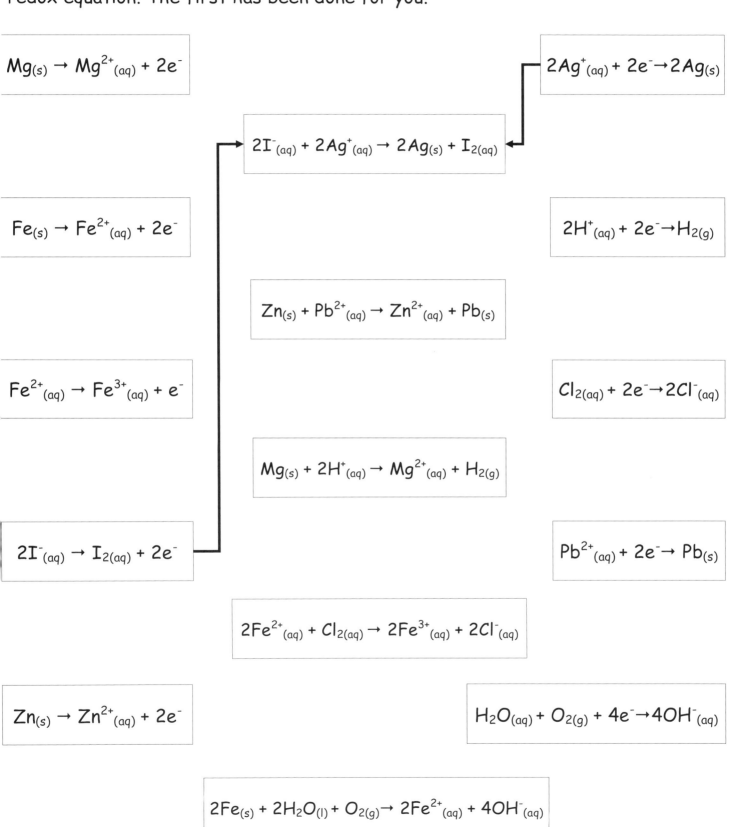

$Mg_{(s)} \rightarrow Mg^{2+}_{(aq)} + 2e^-$

$2Ag^+_{(aq)} + 2e^- \rightarrow 2Ag_{(s)}$

$2I^-_{(aq)} + 2Ag^+_{(aq)} \rightarrow 2Ag_{(s)} + I_{2(aq)}$

$Fe_{(s)} \rightarrow Fe^{2+}_{(aq)} + 2e^-$

$2H^+_{(aq)} + 2e^- \rightarrow H_{2(g)}$

$Zn_{(s)} + Pb^{2+}_{(aq)} \rightarrow Zn^{2+}_{(aq)} + Pb_{(s)}$

$Fe^{2+}_{(aq)} \rightarrow Fe^{3+}_{(aq)} + e^-$

$Cl_{2(aq)} + 2e^- \rightarrow 2Cl^-_{(aq)}$

$Mg_{(s)} + 2H^+_{(aq)} \rightarrow Mg^{2+}_{(aq)} + H_{2(g)}$

$2I^-_{(aq)} \rightarrow I_{2(aq)} + 2e^-$

$Pb^{2+}_{(aq)} + 2e^- \rightarrow Pb_{(s)}$

$2Fe^{2+}_{(aq)} + Cl_{2(aq)} \rightarrow 2Fe^{3+}_{(aq)} + 2Cl^-_{(aq)}$

$Zn_{(s)} \rightarrow Zn^{2+}_{(aq)} + 2e^-$

$H_2O_{(aq)} + O_{2(g)} + 4e^- \rightarrow 4OH^-_{(aq)}$

$2Fe_{(s)} + 2H_2O_{(l)} + O_{2(g)} \rightarrow 2Fe^{2+}_{(aq)} + 4OH^-_{(aq)}$

Quiz Word

Answer the following questions to complete the quiz word and then try and work out what the key phrase in the **bold** boxes should be.

1. Produces electricity by reacting hydrogen with oxygen. (4,4)
2. Ionic solution or paste that completes the circuit. (11)
3. A description of the outer electrons in metallic bonding. (11)
4. Lead-acid and nickel-cadmium batteries are examples of these types of batteries. (12)
5. Atoms or ions gain electrons during this process. (9)
6. Combining oxidation and reduction ½ equations produces one of these equations. (5)
7. Changing the metals in a cell will alter this. (7)

Quiz Word Clue: Another name for a battery

Practice Questions

1. The following cell can be used to make electricity.

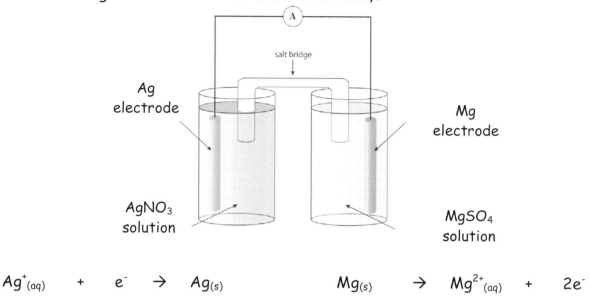

$$Ag^+_{(aq)} + e^- \rightarrow Ag_{(s)} \qquad\qquad Mg_{(s)} \rightarrow Mg^{2+}_{(aq)} + 2e^-$$

a. Combine the 2 ion-electron equations for the electrode reactions to produce a **balanced** REDOX equation.

b. The salt bridge acts as an electrolyte.
   What is an electrolyte?

2. When iron filings are added to a blue copper(II) sulfate solution, the blue colour fades and brown copper metal forms.

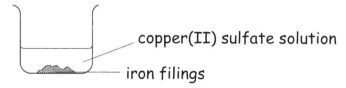

copper(II) sulfate solution

iron filings

The ion-electron equations for the oxidation and reduction reactions are

$$Fe_{(s)} \rightarrow Fe^{2+}_{(aq)} + 2e^-$$
$$Cu^{2+}_{(aq)} + 2e^- \rightarrow Cu_{(s)}$$

Combine the two ion-electron equations to give the redox equation for the reaction.

3.

In a dry cell zinc forms one of the electrodes:

ai.   Write the ion electron ½ equation for the oxidation of zinc atoms.

ii.   Suggest why a zinc dry cell eventually runs out of charge.

b.   The voltages of cells can be measured. Some voltages of cells in which different metals are connected to copper are shown in the table.

Metal connected to copper	Voltage (V)
Iron	0·44
Lead	0·13
Lithium	3·02

If zinc is attached to the copper, predict whether the voltage produced would be more or less than the voltage produced with lithium attached to the copper.

4.   Titanium metal is used in some supersonic aircraft.

Titanium is extracted from its ore in the Kroll process. One step in this process involves the displacement of titanium from its chloride by magnesium metal.

The equation is shown.

$$TiCl_4 \quad + \quad 2Mg \quad \rightarrow \quad Ti \quad + \quad 2MgCl_2$$

a.   What does this method of extraction tell you about the reactivity of titanium metal compared to magnesium metal?

b.   During the displacement, magnesium atoms, Mg, form magnesium ions, Mg^{2+}.

Write the ion-electron equation for this change.

c.   The displacement reaction is carried out at a very high temperature in an atmosphere of the noble gas, argon.

Suggest why an argon atmosphere is used.

d.   A mixture of titanium and aluminium is known as Ti6Al4 and is a high strength general purpose alloy used for building the superstructure of aircraft wings.
The composition of the alloy is given in the table below:

Metal	Titanium	Aluminium
Percentage	60	40

A wing strut has a mass of 12kg.

Calculate the mass of titanium in the strut.

Unit 3   Properties of Plastics

ADDITION POLYMERISATION

All plastics are polymers, made from 1000's of small molecules called monomers. If the monomer contains a carbon-carbon double bond, the polymer formed is called an addition polymer. You can identify an addition polymer from its name as they often start with poly- and end in -ene, e.g. polyethene, polystyrene, etc.

If the structure of the monomer or polymer are shown, you can tell it is an addition polymer as the monomer will have a carbon-carbon double bond C=C and the section of polymer will contain 6 carbon atoms with regularly repeating branches.

monomer   polymer

In order to show the addition polymerisation process it helps to convert any monomer into an 'H' shape with the C=C in the middle:

propene   becomes

Three monomers are then drawn to show how they join together in a chain by an addition reaction:

For example propene

polypropene

The repeating unit consists of the first two carbon atoms with all their bonds shown, this can be converted into the original monomer by just putting the double bond back in the middle.

repeating unit   original monomer

CO.._E..SATIO.. POLY¨¨E..ISATIO..

Many natural polymers such as starch, proteins and cellulose are of a type known as condensation polymers. Other examples of this type of polymer are nylon and polyester.

If the structure of the monomer or polymer are shown, you can tell it is a condensation polymer as there are usually two monomers one of which will contain a carboxyl, hydroxyl or amine functional group at both ends. The section of polymer will contain many more than 6 carbons and there will be a C=O appearing at regular intervals along the chain.

monomer   polymer

In order to show the condensation polymerisation process it helps to ignore the rest of the molecule between the two functional groups. Square boxes are often used to represent the rest of the chain:

e.g. polyesters

dicarboxylic acid   diol

The acid and the alcohol group can join together with the loss of the elements to form water. This is exactly the same reaction that occurs when an ester is made, when an alcohol and a carboxylic acid react together.

↓ **condensation polymerisation**

Nylon is a polyamide made by reacting a dicarboxylic acid and a diamine.

a dicarboxylic acid   a diamine

a polyamide

Addition Polymerisation (I)

Link the polymer name to its monomer name and structure. The first one has been done for you.

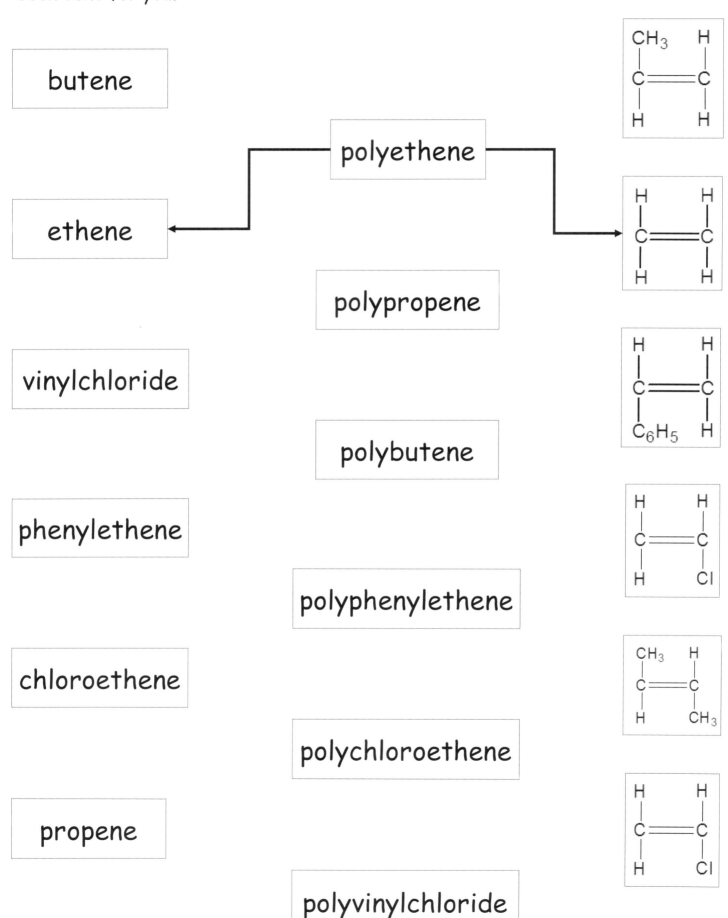

butene

ethene

vinylchloride

phenylethene

chloroethene

propene

polyethene

polypropene

polybutene

polyphenylethene

polychloroethene

polyvinylchloride

Addition Polymerisation (II)

Link the polymer structure to its monomer structure and repeating unit. The first one has been done for you.

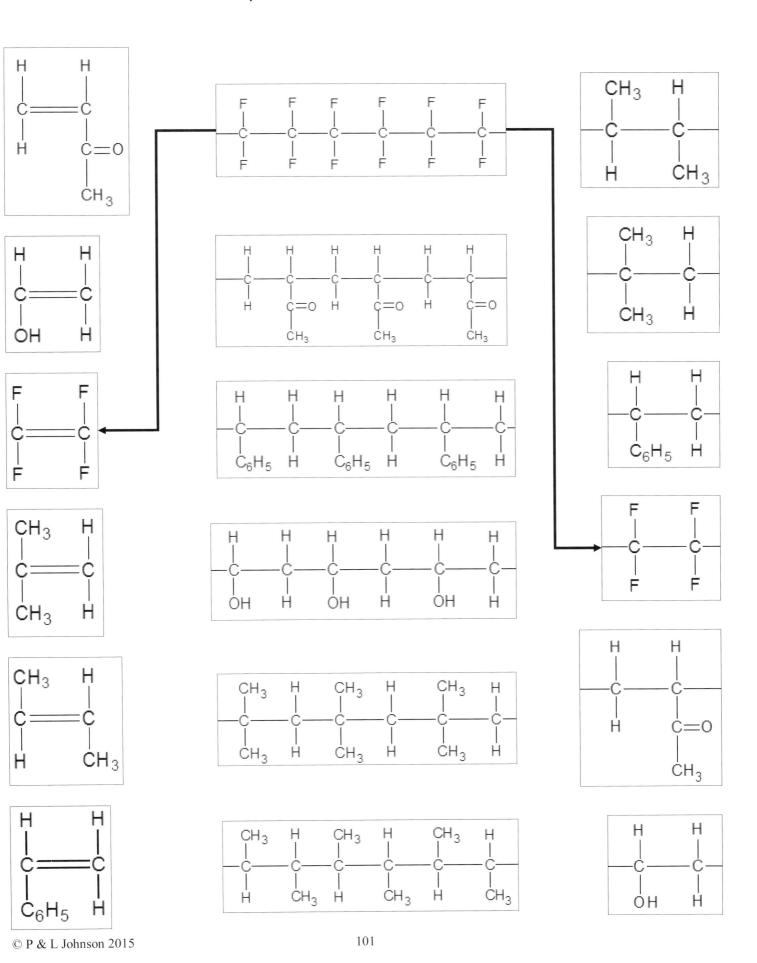

Condensation Polymerisation (I)

Circle any amide or ester links in the following polymers. The first one has been done for you.

Condensation Polymerisation (II)

Identify the letters for the two monomers that were used to form the following condensation polymers shown:

A $HO-\overset{\overset{O}{\|}}{C}-\bigcirc-\overset{\overset{O}{\|}}{C}-OH$

B $HO-\overset{\overset{O}{\|}}{C}-CH_2-CH_2-CH_2-CH_2-\overset{\overset{O}{\|}}{C}-OH$

C $HO-\overset{\overset{O}{\|}}{C}-CH_2-CH_2-CH_2-CH_2-CH_2-CH_2-CH_2-CH_2-\overset{\overset{O}{\|}}{C}-OH$

D $HO-CH_2-CH_2-OH$

E $H_2N-CH_2-CH_2-CH_2-CH_2-CH_2-CH_2-NH_2$

_____ + _____

$-\overset{\overset{O}{\|}}{C}-(CH_2)_4-\overset{\overset{O}{\|}}{C}-\underset{\underset{H}{|}}{N}-(CH_2)_6-\underset{\underset{H}{|}}{N}-\overset{\overset{O}{\|}}{C}-(CH_2)_4-\overset{\overset{O}{\|}}{C}-\underset{\underset{H}{|}}{N}-(CH_2)_6-\underset{\underset{H}{|}}{N}-$

_____ + _____

$-\overset{\overset{O}{\|}}{C}-\bigcirc-\overset{\overset{O}{\|}}{C}-O-CH_2-CH_2-O-\overset{\overset{O}{\|}}{C}-\bigcirc-\overset{\overset{O}{\|}}{C}-O-CH_2-CH_2-O-$

_____ + _____

$-\underset{}{\overset{\overset{H}{|}}{N}}-(CH_2)_6-\overset{\overset{H}{|}}{N}-\underset{\underset{O}{\|}}{C}-(CH_2)_8-\underset{\underset{O}{\|}}{C}-\overset{\overset{H}{|}}{N}-(CH_2)_6-\overset{\overset{H}{|}}{N}-\underset{\underset{O}{\|}}{C}-(CH_2)_8-\underset{\underset{O}{\|}}{C}-$

Repeating Units

Put square brackets around the first repeating unit of the following polymers. The first one has been done for you.

Quiz Word

Answer the following questions to complete the quiz word and then try and work out what the key phrase in the **bold** boxes should be.

1. This is what all plastic materials are called. (8)
2. Type of polymer formed from alkenes. (8)
3. Monomer used to make polystyrene. (7)
4. Small section of the polymer chain that keeps reoccurring. (9,4)
5. Small molecule that join together in long chains to form polymers. (7)
6. What's broken when an addition polymer forms. (6,4)
7. Common name for many polyamides. (5)
8. Functional group that joins up to form either ester or amide links in condensation polymers. (8)

Quiz Word Clue: Proteins and plastics like nylon are examples of this

Practice Questions

1. Poly(ethenyl ethanoate) is a polymer that is used to manufacture PVA glue, a section of it is shown below:

$$-\overset{\displaystyle H}{\underset{\displaystyle H}{\overset{|}{\underset{|}{C}}}}-\overset{\displaystyle OCOCH_3}{\underset{\displaystyle H}{\overset{|}{\underset{|}{C}}}}-\overset{\displaystyle H}{\underset{\displaystyle H}{\overset{|}{\underset{|}{C}}}}-\overset{\displaystyle OCOCH_3}{\underset{\displaystyle H}{\overset{|}{\underset{|}{C}}}}-\overset{\displaystyle H}{\underset{\displaystyle H}{\overset{|}{\underset{|}{C}}}}-\overset{\displaystyle OCOCH_3}{\underset{\displaystyle H}{\overset{|}{\underset{|}{C}}}}-$$

ai. Draw the structural formula for the repeating unit found in this polymer.

ii. Draw the structural formula for the monomer used to make this polymer.

b. What type of polymer is poly(ethenyl ethanoate)?

2. Nylon is a polymer.
   A section showing four monomer units linked together:

$$-\overset{O}{\overset{||}{C}}-(CH_2)_4-\overset{O}{\overset{||}{C}}-\underset{\underset{H}{|}}{N}-(CH_2)_6-\underset{\underset{H}{|}}{N}-\overset{O}{\overset{||}{C}}-(CH_2)_4-\overset{O}{\overset{||}{C}}-\underset{\underset{H}{|}}{N}-(CH_2)_6-\underset{\underset{H}{|}}{N}-$$

a. Show on the structure the repeating unit.

b. Draw one of the monomer units.

3.   Non stick frying pans contain a thin layer of the plastic PTFE.

a.   PTFE is a polymer made from the monomer shown.

$$F \quad F$$
$$| \quad\quad |$$
$$C = C$$
$$| \quad\quad |$$
$$F \quad F$$

Draw a section of the PTFE polymer, showing three monomer units joined together.

b.   Name this type of polymerisation reaction.

4.   Kevlar is very strong and is used to make high performance tennis racket strings. It is made from the following monomers.

a.   Draw the structure of the repeating unit formed from these two monomers.

b.   Name this type of polymerisation reaction.

Unit 3 Fertilisers

THE HABER PROCESS

The Haber Process is used to make ammonia which is the starting material for many fertilisers as well as dyes and explosives.

The reaction involves reacting nitrogen, from air, and hydrogen, obtained from natural gas, at high pressure and using an **iron catalyst**. The **catalyst speeds up the reaction** and allows it to occur at reasonable temperatures and pressures. **The reaction is reversible** and so it is important to get the right conditions to maximise its production.

$$N_{2(g)} \quad + \quad 3H_{2(g)} \quad \rightleftharpoons \quad 2NH_{3(g)}$$

Ammonia is a very soluble gas that dissolves in water to form ammonium hydroxide, an alkali.

$$NH_{3(g)} \quad + \quad H_2O_{(l)} \quad \rightarrow \quad NH_4^+OH^-_{(aq)}$$

Ammonia can be converted into nitric acid by the Ostwald Process using its reaction with oxygen and water.

$$\text{ammonia} \quad \xrightarrow{\text{(oxygen \& water)}} \quad \text{nitric acid (HNO}_3\text{)}$$

MAKING FERTILISERS

Plants require 3 nutrients, nitrogen, phosphorus and potassium. Fertilisers are mixtures of salts containing these elements and are often called NPK fertilisers.

To make a salt, an acid is neutralised by a base. Ammonium nitrate is a salt containing a large quantity of nitrogen and is made by reacting ammonium hydroxide with nitric acid.

To make salts with phosphorus you need to neutralise phosphoric acid and to make potassium salts you need to neutralise an acid using a base containing potassium.

NPK VALUES

What is the % of nitrogen in the fertiliser, ammonium nitrate, NH_4NO_3? Work out its gram formula mass

NH_4NO_3

$3 \times 16 = 48$
$1 \times 14 = 14$
$4 \times 1 = 4$
$1 \times 14 = 14$

GFM (1mole) = 80g

Out of this 80g total, what % is nitrogen?

Mass nitrogen = 28g out of the total of 80g

% mass of nitrogen = $\dfrac{28}{80} \times 100$

= 35%

NPK Values - % Composition

Work out the % mass of each of the nutrients in each NPK fertilisers. The first one has been done for you.

$(NH_4)_3PO_4$

% N = (3x14)/GFM = 42/149x100
% P = 31/ GFM = 31/149x100
% K = 0

% N = 28%
% P = 21%
% K = 0%

K_3PO_4

% N =
% P =
% K =

KNO_3

% N =
% P =
% K =

NH_4NO_3

% N =
% P =
% K =

K_2SO_4

% N =
% P =
% K =

Fertiliser Salts

Join the acid and base that could make each of the fertiliser salts shown. The first one has been done for you.

Fertiliser Salt

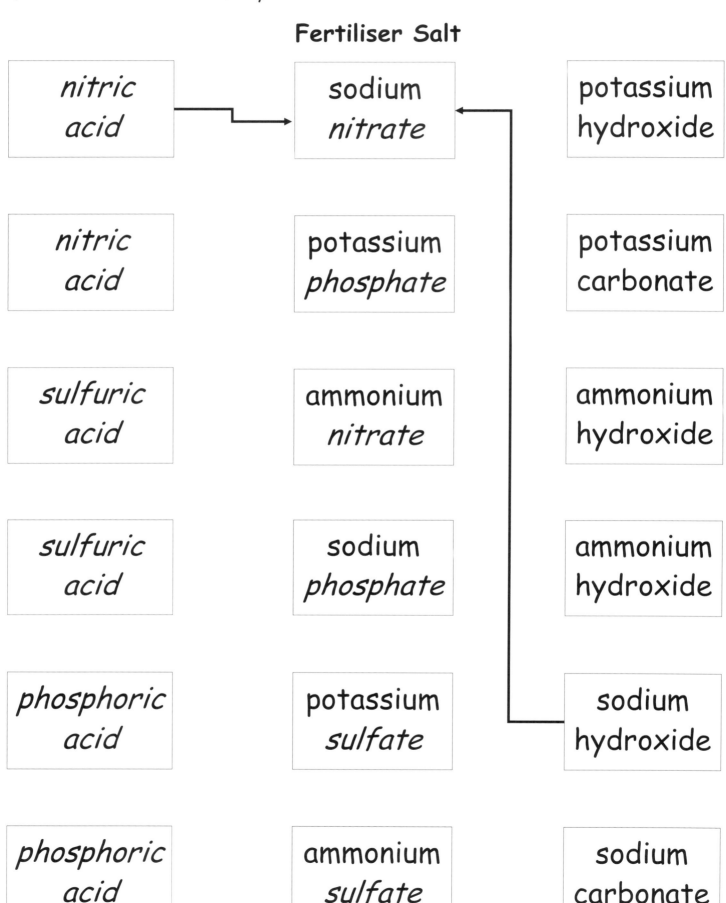

nitric acid	sodium nitrate	potassium hydroxide
nitric acid	potassium phosphate	potassium carbonate
sulfuric acid	ammonium nitrate	ammonium hydroxide
sulfuric acid	sodium phosphate	ammonium hydroxide
phosphoric acid	potassium sulfate	sodium hydroxide
phosphoric acid	ammonium sulfate	sodium carbonate

Making A Fertiliser Salt

Using any of the pieces of equipment and chemicals given in the box below, design an experiment that could produce a dry fertiliser salt containing **any two** of the essential nutrients.

Then calculate the NPK values for your fertiliser.

beakers	filter paper	evaporating basin
filter funnel	measuring cylinders	potassium carbonate
	ammonium hydroxide	Bunsen burner
copper(II) oxide	hydrochloric acid	phosphoric acid
nitric acid	dropping pipette	pH paper
	universal indicator	

Making Ammonium Nitrate

At the start of the process oxygen is reacted with ammonia to form nitrogen monoxide and water. The nitrogen monoxide is further reacted with oxygen and forms nitrogen dioxide. When this dissolves in water it forms nitric acid and more nitrogen monoxide, which is recycled. The nitric acid is neutralised with ammonium hydroxide and the resulting salt solution evaporated to form ammonium nitrate fertiliser.

Use the above information to complete the table below:

Process	Reactants	Products
oxidation of ammonia	ammonia &	nitrogen monoxide &
further oxidation of nitrogen monoxide	& oxygen	
dissolving	nitrogen dioxide & water	
neutralisation	& ammonium hydroxide	& water

Quiz Word

Answer the following questions to complete the quiz word and then try and work out what the key phrase in the **bold** boxes should be.

1. This speeds up a reaction but isn't used up in the process. (8)
2. Gas used to make ammonia that is made from natural gas. (8)
3. Gas used to make ammonia obtained from air. (8)
4. Metal used as a catalyst in the making of ammonia. (4)
5. Ammonia is the starting point of making this important chemical for agriculture. (10)
6. Making ammonia is an example of this type of reaction. (10)

Practice Questions

1. Nitric acid $HNO_{3(aq)}$ can be made by using ammonia gas. Ammonia is made by reacting nitrogen and hydrogen. Often the hydrogen is manufactured from natural gas.

ai. Suggest a source for the nitrogen gas used to make ammonia.

ii. What is the name of the process used to make ammonia?

b. When nitric acid reacts with ammonium hydroxide a common fertiliser is formed.

   Write the ionic formula of the salt formed by the reaction of nitric acid and ammonium hydroxide.

c. Another common fertiliser made from nitric acid is potassium nitrate.

i. Suggest what is reacted with nitric acid to form potassium nitrate.

ii. What is the % mass of nitrogen in potassium nitrate, KNO_3?

2. Ammonia is manufactured using the Haber Process. In order to make the process more efficient a catalyst is used.

ai. Name the catalyst used.

ii. Which two elements are used to make ammonia?

b. When ammonia is oxidised and then dissolved in water, an important acid is formed.

What is the name of the acid.

c. Ammonium nitrate is a very common fertiliser.

In the space below describe how a pure dry sample of this salt could be made in a lab using nitric acid and ammonium hydroxide solution.

Unit 3 Nuclear Chemistry

TYPES OF RADIOACTIVITY

Some isotopes, particularly those with atomic numbers greater than 82 are unstable. They can become more stable by emitting alpha, beta or gamma radiation.

Alpha - given the symbol α or ^4_2He as it is a helium nucleus.

Beta - given the symbol β or $^{\ 0}_{-1}e^-$ as it is a high energy electron.

Gamma - given the symbol γ it is a high energy electromagnetic wave caused by a rearrangement of the protons and neutrons in the nucleus.

Properties

Radioactivity	Mass (a.m.u.)	Charge	Penetrating Power	Ionising damage
alpha	4	+	Stopped by thin paper	High
beta	0	-	Stopped by a sheet of aluminium	Medium
gamma	0	0	Stopped by thick lead or concrete	Low

NUCLEAR EQUATIONS

These equations show what happens to the radioactive isotope or **radioisotope** when it decays. They show the parent isotope, the daughter product and the radiation emitted. It is important when writing nuclear equations to make sure that the total mass number and total atomic number (or nuclear charge) is the same on both sides of the equation.

Alpha decay

$$^{238}_{92}U \rightarrow \ ^4_2He + \ ^{234}_{90}Th$$

Beta decay

$$^{234}_{91}Pa \rightarrow \ ^{\ 0}_{-1}e^- + \ ^{234}_{92}U$$

Gamma decay
As there is no change in the isotope's actual mass or atomic number, nuclear equations are not normally shown.

HALF-LIFE

This is the time it takes for half of the number of radioactive nuclei in a sample to decay. It is fixed and a constant for each particular radioactive isotope. If the mass, activity or number of atoms, for a particular radioactive isotope, is plotted against time an exponential decay curve can be drawn and used to work out the half-life of that isotope.

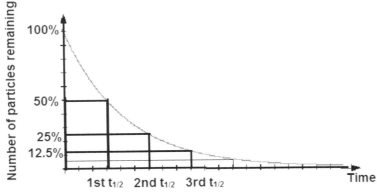

^{14}C is naturally found in all living things, it has a half-life of 5730 years. If a skeleton of a body was found and the quantity of ^{14}C measured and found to be 12.5% of what its level in a human bone is today, we can calculate how old the bone must be:

$$100\% \quad \xrightarrow{t_{1/2}} \quad 50\% \quad \xrightarrow{t_{1/2}} \quad 25\% \quad \xrightarrow{t_{1/2}} \quad 12.5\%$$

The ^{14}C has decayed over 3 half lives each lasting 5730 years, making the bone 17,190 years old.

USES OF RADIOISOTOPES

There are several properties of radiation that make it very useful:

- Radiation is easy to detect even in tiny amounts and so we can use it to trace where water and other substances travel.
- Radiation can penetrate solid objects and so it can be used to look inside things in the same way X-rays are used to look inside you.
- Radiation can destroy living cells, this means it can be used for sterilizing things and for killing cancerous cells in humans.
- Some radioisotopes can be made to split up and when the atom splits it releases a huge amount of energy that can be used to produce electricity.

Examples:

Cobalt-60 - Used to treat deep seated tumours

Americium-241 - Used in smoke detectors

Technetium-99m - Used as a medical tracer

Uranium-235 - Used in nuclear power stations

Types of Radioactivity

Using the information in the table below, complete the second table giving information about the different types of radioactivity:

alpha	γ	0	$^{4}_{2}He$	$^{0}_{-1}e^{-}$
gamma	β	+2	-1	4

Type of radiation	Symbol	Composition	Charge	Mass (amu)
	α			
beta				0
		electromagnetic wave		0

Chemical Misconceptions

A student has completed diagrams about the penetrating power and electrical charges of the different types of radioactivity, but they have made a complete mess of it. Complete the second two diagrams correctly:

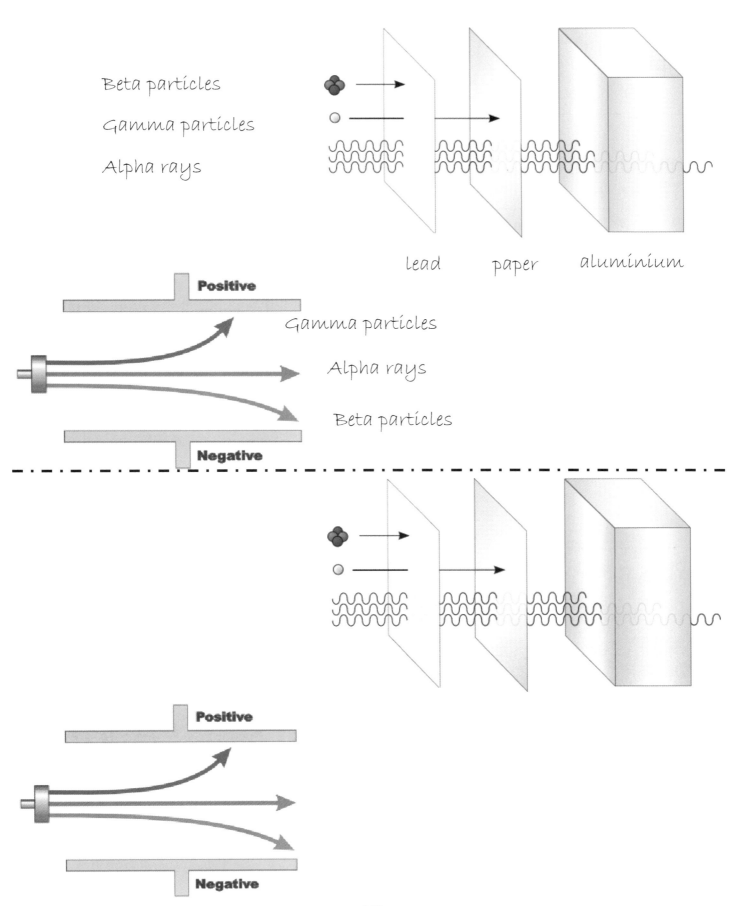

Beta particles

Gamma particles

Alpha rays

lead   paper   aluminium

Positive

Gamma particles

Alpha rays

Beta particles

Negative

Positive

Negative

Nuclear Equations (I)

Identify the daughter product from the decay of a radioactive isotope and draw the connecting line to it. The first one has been done for you.

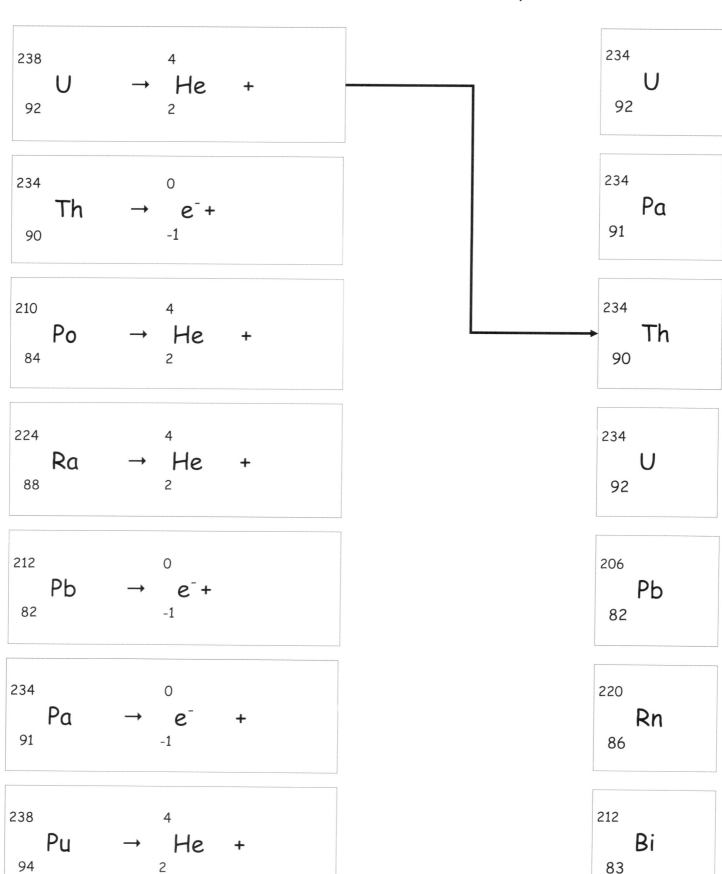

$$^{238}_{92}U \rightarrow {}^{4}_{2}He +$$

$$^{234}_{90}Th \rightarrow {}^{0}_{-1}e^{-} +$$

$$^{210}_{84}Po \rightarrow {}^{4}_{2}He +$$

$$^{224}_{88}Ra \rightarrow {}^{4}_{2}He +$$

$$^{212}_{82}Pb \rightarrow {}^{0}_{-1}e^{-} +$$

$$^{234}_{91}Pa \rightarrow {}^{0}_{-1}e^{-} +$$

$$^{238}_{94}Pu \rightarrow {}^{4}_{2}He +$$

$$^{234}_{92}U$$

$$^{234}_{91}Pa$$

$$^{234}_{90}Th$$

$$^{234}_{92}U$$

$$^{206}_{82}Pb$$

$$^{220}_{86}Rn$$

$$^{212}_{83}Bi$$

Nuclear Equations (II)

Identify the type of radiation emitted by looking at the nuclear decay equations. The first one has been done for you.

$$^{228}_{90}\text{Th} \rightarrow {}^{224}_{88}\text{Ra}$$

alpha

$$^{99m}_{43}\text{Tc} \rightarrow {}^{99}_{43}\text{Tc}$$

_____

$$^{14}_{6}\text{C} \rightarrow {}^{14}_{7}\text{N}$$

_____

$$^{60}_{27}\text{Co} \rightarrow {}^{60}_{27}\text{Co}$$

_____

$$^{222}_{86}\text{Rn} \rightarrow {}^{218}_{84}\text{Po}$$

_____

$$^{24}_{11}\text{Na} \rightarrow {}^{24}_{12}\text{Mg}$$

_____

$$^{24m}_{12}\text{Mg} \rightarrow {}^{24}_{12}\text{Mg}$$

_____

Half Lives

Use the radioactive decay curves to work out the half life of each isotope and then answer the second question.

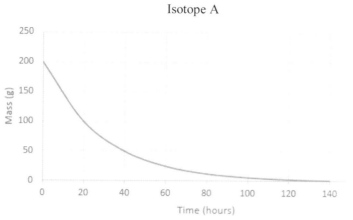

Half-Life =

Mass after 40 hours =

Half-Life =

Atoms after 10 hours =

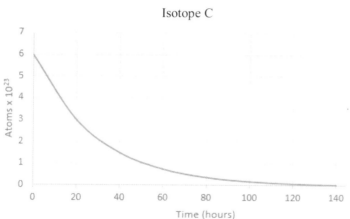

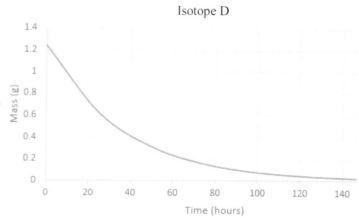

Half-Life =

Atoms after 3 ½-lives =

Half-Life =

Mass after 3 ½-lives =

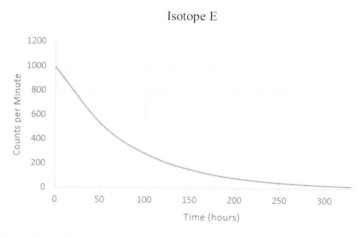

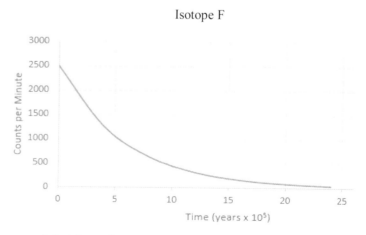

Half-Life =

Number of ½-lives when count rate is 125 counts per minute =

Half-Life =

Count rate after 2 ½-lives =

Uses of Radioisotopes

Use the following descriptions of how a particular radioisotope is used and then try to identify the most appropriate from the list below:

A— Smoke Detector: The radiation ionises the air particles inside the smoke detector. This allows a small electric current to flow. If there is a fire, smoke particles prevents the radiation ionising the air particles, causing the current to drop, setting off the alarm.

B— Removing deep seated tumours: This treatment can be used anywhere on the body. It is particularly useful in brain tumour patients because it is so precise. The therapy allows the doctor to deliver higher doses of radiation to the tumour with limited damage to the surrounding healthy tissue and/or organs.

C— Controlling paper thickness: The isotope gives off radiation, some of which passes through the paper as it passes beneath. The radiation detector is placed below the conveyor belt. The detector measures the amount of radiation passing through the sheeting and a computer controls the machinery to maintain the right thickness.

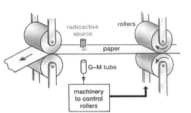

Isotope	State	Type of Radiation	½ Life
polonium-210	solid	alpha	138 days
Amercium-241	solid	alpha	434 years
hydrogen-3	gas	beta	12 years
strontium-90	solid	beta	28 years
cobalt-60	solid	gamma	5 years
xenon-133	gas	gamma	5 days

A— uses _____ because_____

_____

B— uses_____ because_____

_____

C— uses_____ because_____

_____

Quiz Word

Answer the following questions to complete the quiz word and then try and work out what the key phrase in the **bold** boxes should be.

1. The time it takes for half a sample of radioactive atoms to decay. (4-4)
2. A type of radiation with no mass or charge. (5, 4)
3. Charge on a beta particle. (8)
4. A sheet of this will stop alpha particles. (5)
5. Name given to an atom with a particular atomic mass that is radioactive. (12)
6. A disease that can both be caused and cured by radiation. (6)

Practice Questions

1. Polonium-210 decays by alpha emission.

a. Complete the nuclear equation for the alpha decay of polonium-210.

$$^{210}_{84}Po \rightarrow$$

A fresh sample of polonium-210 was placed in a plastic lunchbox. A radiation detector was held 5cm away from the box.
Why was there **no** alpha radiation detected?

c. Polonium-210 has a half-life of 138 days. What mass of polonium-210 would be left from a 1.0g sample after 414 days?

2. Uranium-238 is a radioactive isotope that decays to thorium 234 via alpha decay. The thorium is still radioactive and decays to protactinium-234.

$$^{234}_{90}Th \rightarrow ^{234}_{91}Pa + X$$

a. Identify particle **X**.

b. Protactinium decays by beta decay to form another isotope of uranium.
What is the mass number of this isotope of uranium?

c. Thorium-234 has a half-life of 24 days.
If a sample of thorium-234 is left for 48 days, what fraction of the sample would remain?

3. Carbon dating can be used to estimate the age of clothing and other artefacts found in archaeological sites.
The graph shows how the count rate of a sample of radioactive carbon-14 changes over a period of time.

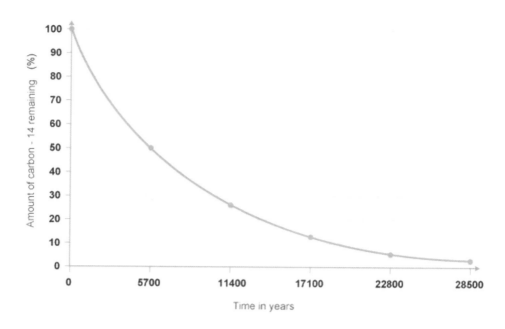

a. Use the graph to find the approximate half-life of carbon-14.

b. Carbon-14 decays by beta-emission.
Write the nuclide notation of the isotope formed.

c. A piece of leather discovered in a cave was found to have only 12.5% of the number of carbon-14 atoms compared to a piece of modern leather. Approximately how old was the piece of leather?

4. Some of the rocks found in Scotland are the oldest in the world, their age can be determined by measuring the ratio of argon-40 and potassium-40 atoms present in a sample of the rock.

a. Each potassium-40 atom can emit a single positron particle to form an argon-40 atom.

$$^{40}_{19}K \rightarrow ^{40}_{18}Ar + positron$$

If the symbol for a positron is β^+, write the nuclide notation for a positron.

b. If 75% of the potassium-40 atoms originally present in a rock sample were found to have undergone radioactive decay to form argon-40. Calculate the age of the rock, in years, if the half-life of potassium-40 is 1.26 billion years.

Unit 3   Chemical Analysis

ENVIRONMENTAL ANALYSIS

Below are some examples of the techniques that can be used and what pollutants they might identify:

- pH measurement using universal indicator or a pH probe, to measure acidity.
- Acid/base titration to find concentration of acid or alkali.
- Precipitation reactions to identify presence of specific metal ions.
- Flame tests to identify presence of specific metal ions.

ACID/BASE TITRATIONS

pH paper or universal indicator can be used to measure the pH of water samples. You can also use pH meters or probes which give a digital reading for the pH of the water.

A titration is an example of quantitative analysis where the concentration of an acidic pollutant can be measured.

Look back at your notes on acids and bases to see how the technique and calculation is carried out. Also page 52 in this book.

FLAME TESTS

When metal atoms or ions are heated by a flame, their electrons can become excited and are promoted to higher energy levels. The excited electrons are unstable and fall back down to their original position releasing the energy in the form of coloured light.

Page 6 of the data booklet has a table with some common metals and their flame colours.

Metal	Flame colour
Copper	Blue/Green
Strontium	Red
Sodium	Yellow
Potassium	Lilac

PRECIPITATION REACTIONS

Certain metal compounds are very soluble in water, such as silver nitrate, but if it mixes with another solution containing a different compound, such as sodium chloride, a reaction can occur where the silver forms an insoluble compound, silver chloride and **a solid called a precipitate forms. This is known as a precipitation reaction** and it can be used to identify the presence of certain metals in the water.
e.g.

$$AgNO_{3(aq)} + NaCl_{(aq)}$$

$$NaNO_{3(aq)} + AgCl_{(s)}$$

Acid/Base Titrations (I)

Water polluted by acids can be analysed using an acid/alkali titration. Use some of the following from the word bank to fully label the titration apparatus below:

pipette   burette   beaker   conical flask   indicator

measuring cylinder   white tile   polluted water

alkali of known concentration   acid of known concentration

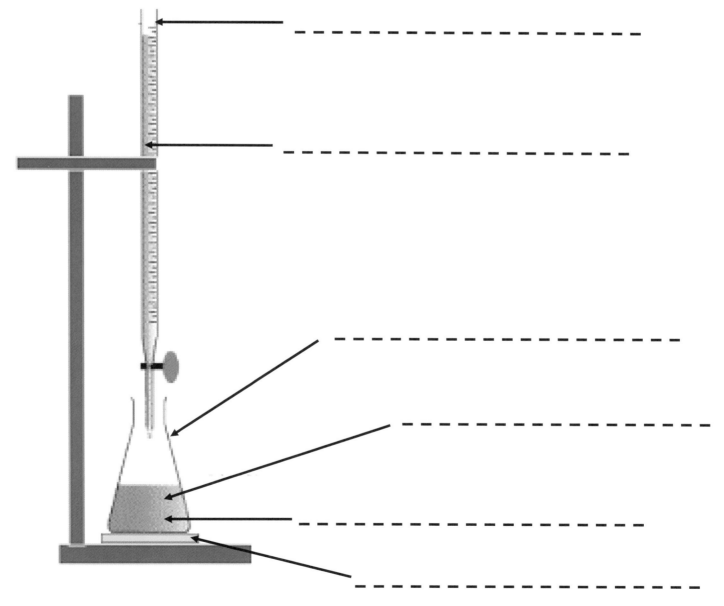

Acid/Base Titrations (II)

Water polluted by acids can be analysed using an acid/alkali titration. Order the following descriptions into the correct sequence of how to use an acid /alkali titration to analyse a sample of polluted water:

A. Add a few drops of indicator.	B. Stop and record the volume when the indicator changes colour.	C. Make sure the colour change occurs with the addition of just one drop.
D. Repeat the experiment but this time add only a drop of alkali at a time near to the end point.	E. Use a pipette to measure out 25cm^3 of the water sample into a conical flask.	F. Repeat accurately until you get two concordant results.
G. Run in 1cm^3 of the alkali at a time, swirling the flask.	H. Find the average of the two concordant results.	I. Fill a burette with an alkali of known concentration.

Correct Order:

____ ____ ____ ____ ____ ____ ____ ____ ____

Correct Glassware

Draw a link between the glassware, its name and what it is used for.

	measuring cylinder	used to mix chemicals in
	conical flask	used to accurately measure a variable volume from 0-50cm^3
	beaker	used to accurately measure a fixed volume
	burette	used to swirl solutions in a titration
	pipette	used to measure a variable volume from 0-100cm^3

Precipitation Reactions

Connect the two solutions that would form the precipitate in the middle. The first one has been done for you.

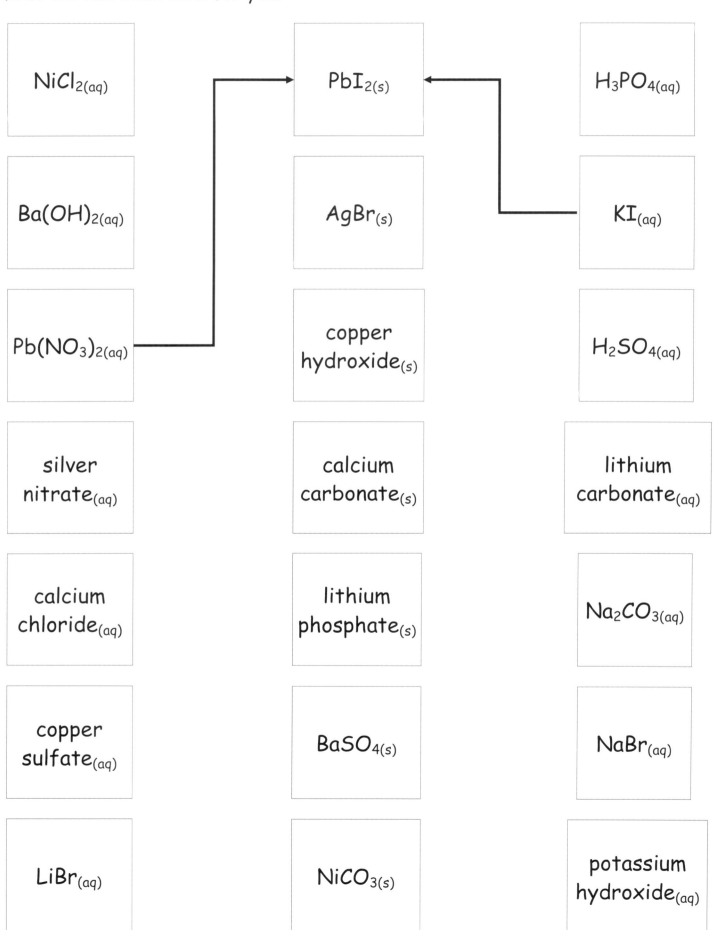

NiCl$_{2(aq)}$	PbI$_{2(s)}$	H$_3$PO$_{4(aq)}$
Ba(OH)$_{2(aq)}$	AgBr$_{(s)}$	KI$_{(aq)}$
Pb(NO$_3$)$_{2(aq)}$	copper hydroxide$_{(s)}$	H$_2$SO$_{4(aq)}$
silver nitrate$_{(aq)}$	calcium carbonate$_{(s)}$	lithium carbonate$_{(aq)}$
calcium chloride$_{(aq)}$	lithium phosphate$_{(s)}$	Na$_2$CO$_{3(aq)}$
copper sulfate$_{(aq)}$	BaSO$_{4(s)}$	NaBr$_{(aq)}$
LiBr$_{(aq)}$	NiCO$_{3(s)}$	potassium hydroxide$_{(aq)}$

Flame Colours

From the flame colours shown below select a likely colour for the metal salts given, you may wish to use p6 of your data booklet to help:

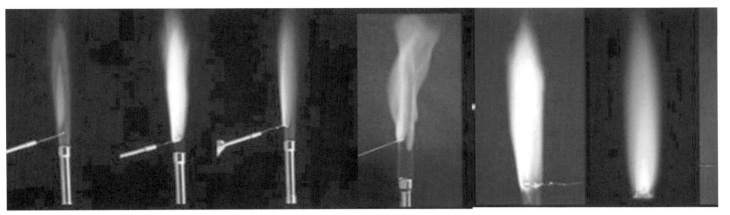

Red	yellow	lilac	orange-red	green	blue-green
A	B	C	D	E	F

Metal Salt	Flame Colour
potassium nitrate	
copper sulfate	
lithium chloride	
sodium chloride	
barium nitrate	
strontium chloride	
calcium chloride	
copper chloride	
sodium nitrate	
potassium sulfate	
calcium sulfate	

Quiz Word

Answer the following questions to complete the quiz word and then try and work out what the key phrase in the **bold** boxes should be.

1. Used to identify the end-point in a titration. (9)
2. Formed when an insoluble product is produced. (11)
3. Another name for an alkali. (4)
4. Become excited during a flame test. (9)
5. Used to measure accurately a variable volume of solution. (7)
6. Flame colour associated with compounds containing potassium ions. (5)
7. Type of solution used in precipitation reactions. (5)

Quiz Word Clue: Used to calculate the concentration of acid in polluted water.

Practice Questions

1. A container of hydrochloric acid was accidently spilt in a field. A student wanted to work out how much acid a sample of the soil contained. She mixed 10g of soil in 50cm³ of water and left it to settle overnight. She then carefully filtered the mixture and collected the filtrate in a conical flask.

   She set up the following apparatus in order to find out the concentration of acid in the water sample.

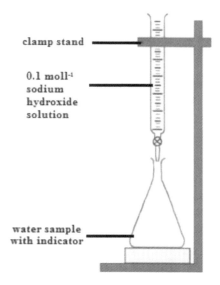

a. What name is given to this experimental procedure?

b. Write a balanced **ionic** equation for the reaction.

c. She used 25cm³ of 0.1 moll⁻¹ sodium hydroxide to completely neutralise the 50cm³ sample of water.

   What was the concentration of the hydrochloric acid solution made using the soil sample?

_____moll⁻¹

2. The concentration of chloride ions in water affects the ability of some plants to grow.

A student investigated the concentration of chloride ions in the water at various points along the river Tay. The concentration of chloride ions in water can be determined by reacting the chloride ions with silver ions.

$$Ag^+_{(aq)} + Cl^-_{(aq)} \rightarrow AgCl_{(s)}$$

A 20 cm^3 water sample gave a precipitate of silver chloride with a mass of 1·435 g.

a. Calculate the number of moles of silver chloride, AgCl, present in this sample.

Show your working clearly.

_____ moles

b. Using your answer to part (a), calculate the concentration, in moll^{-1}, of chloride ions in this sample.

Show your working clearly.

_____moll^{-1}

3. Sodium carbonate solution can be added to the water in swimming pools to neutralise the acidic effects of chlorine.

A student carried out a titration experiment to determine the concentration of a sodium carbonate solution.

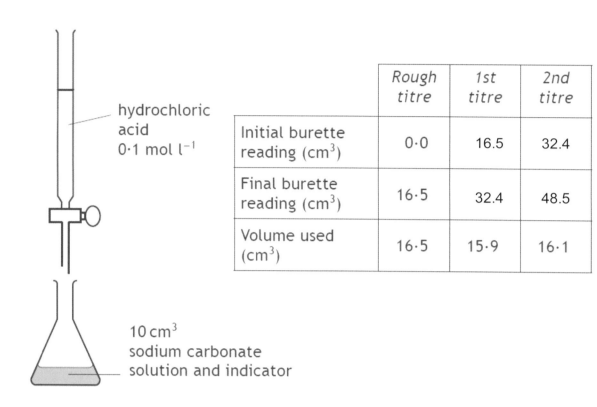

	Rough titre	1st titre	2nd titre
Initial burette reading (cm^3)	0·0	16.5	32.4
Final burette reading (cm^3)	16·5	32.4	48.5
Volume used (cm^3)	16·5	15·9	16·1

hydrochloric acid
0·1 mol l^{-1}

10 cm^3
sodium carbonate
solution and indicator

a. Using the results in the table, calculate the average volume, in cm^3, of hydrochloric acid required to neutralise the sodium carbonate solution.

_____cm^3

b. The equation for the reaction is

$$2HCl + Na_2CO_3 \rightarrow 2NaCl + CO_2 + H_2O$$

Using your answer from part (a) calculate the concentration, in $mol l^{-1}$, of the sodium carbonate solution.

Show your working clearly.

_____$mol l^{-1}$

"Use Your Knowledge of Chemistry" Questions (I)

These type of questions are quite difficult. Remember you need to use chemistry to answer the question, so it is important to identify what parts of the course are relevant to the question.

Use the box of chemical ideas you have covered at National 5 to link as many of them as you can to the "use your knowledge of chemistry" questions. There may be more than one idea that is related, the first one has been done for you.

```
┌─────────────────────────────────────────────────────────────────────┐
│                          Chemical Ideas                             │
│                                                                      │
│   rates of reaction    Periodic Table    atomic structure    types of bonding │
│                                                                      │
│        properties of substances    acids & bases    neutralisation   │
│                                                                      │
│      hydrocarbons    fuels & burning    reactions of hydrocarbons    │
│                                                                      │
│    alcohols    carboxylic acids    esters    plastics    metals      │
│                                                                      │
│     extraction of metals    electricity    redox    radioactivity    │
│                                                                      │
│        uses of radioisotopes    fertilisers    chemical analysis     │
└─────────────────────────────────────────────────────────────────────┘
```

1. Burning ethanol as a fuel is better for the environment than burning petrol.
   Using your knowledge of chemistry comment on the accuracy of this statement.
   Hydrocarbons, fuels & burning, alcohols and acids & bases

2. Leicester is a city in England that boasts that it is Britain's first nuclear free zone.
   Using your knowledge of chemistry explain whether this is likely to be true.

3. A new element has been discovered with an electron arrangement of 2,8,18,32,32,18,8,1.
   Using your knowledge of chemistry suggest where in the Periodic Table it should be placed. Predict its chemical and physical properties giving your reasons.

4. Three metals magnesium, iron and tin all look the same, being silvery grey. Using your knowledge of chemistry suggest a method that they could all be identified, that could be performed in a school lab.

5. An unknown compound containing carbon has been found. Using your knowledge of chemistry suggest a number of tests that could be used to help identify the type of compound it is.

"Use Your Knowledge of Chemistry" Questions (II)

Having identified the areas of the course the question is linked to, it's important to answer the question using **chemistry and chemical terms**, explaining your ideas.

These type of questions are a chance to "show off" your knowledge of chemistry, so try not to be too brief. You don't have to give a perfect answer to get full marks but it should show a good comprehension of the chemistry of the situation and provide a logically correct answer to the question posed. This type of response might include a statement of the principles involved, a relationship or an equation, and the application of these to respond to the problem. Diagrams can also help explain your thinking in a clearer way.

Look at the following possible ideas linked to the question given, some of which could be expanded on to give a good answer.

Try and do the same for question 5.

4. *Three metals magnesium, iron and tin all look the same, being silvery grey. Using your knowledge of chemistry suggest a method that they could all be identified, that could be performed in a school lab.*

    Melting points   reactions with water   reaction with acid
        reaction with oxygen   displacement reactions   density
    electrochemical cell   direction of current   size of voltage
    redox equations   chemical equations   electron arrangement

5. An unknown compound containing carbon has been found. Using your knowledge of chemistry suggest a number of tests that could be used to help identify the type of compound it is.

"Use Your Knowledge of Chemistry" Questions (III)

Below are some examples of pupil answers to the following question:

4. *Three metals magnesium, iron and tin all look the same, being silvery grey. Using your knowledge of chemistry suggest a method that they could all be identified, that could be performed in a school lab.*

Try to mark them using the following guidelines:

3 marks: The maximum available mark would be awarded to a student who has demonstrated a good understanding of the chemistry involved. **2 marks**: The student has demonstrated a reasonable understanding of the chemistry involved. **1 mark**: The student has demonstrated a limited understanding of the chemistry involved. **0 mark**: the student has demonstrated no understanding of the chemistry involved.

In the space below each answer try to explain how you arrived at that mark; what did the pupil put down that was correct and what was missing from their answer?

Pupil 1
Burn them and see which reacts the most. That will be magnesium, the least reactive is tin.

Pupil 2
Set up three electrochemical cells with copper as one electrode and the metals magnesium, iron and tin as the other. Use copper sulfate as the electrolyte. Record the voltage produced. The biggest will be magnesium, the next biggest iron and the smallest tin. This is because magnesium is closer to copper in the electrochemical series than iron which is closer than tin.

Pupil 3
Use a magnet the tin will stick to it, the others won't. Drop them in water the one that reacts with a bang is magnesium.

Pupil 4
Make up three solutions, one magnesium nitrate, one iron nitrate and one tin nitrate. Add a piece of each metal to them and see which has a displacement reaction. Nothing should happen in the magnesium nitrate; the magnesium will be the only one to react with the iron nitrate.

$Mg + Fe^{2+} \rightarrow Mg^{2+} + Fe$

Add the other two metals to the tin nitrate, the iron will be the only one to react with the tin nitrate.

$Fe + Sn^{2+} \rightarrow Fe^{2+} + Sn$

Creating Mind Maps and Spider Diagrams

Some people remember diagrams and pictures far better than words.
Mind maps and spider diagrams are a good way to make your revision material more visual and easier to see the link between ideas.

Have a central theme and then draw lines from it to the key ideas, you can then add branches or lines to these main ideas to add more detail. Use drawings and images to help you remember and make it visually more interesting.

Below is an example of a spider diagram on bonding, with some key areas but no diagrams or images. Try copying it out on a larger piece of paper, add more ideas and add diagrams, images and tables to help explain each of these:

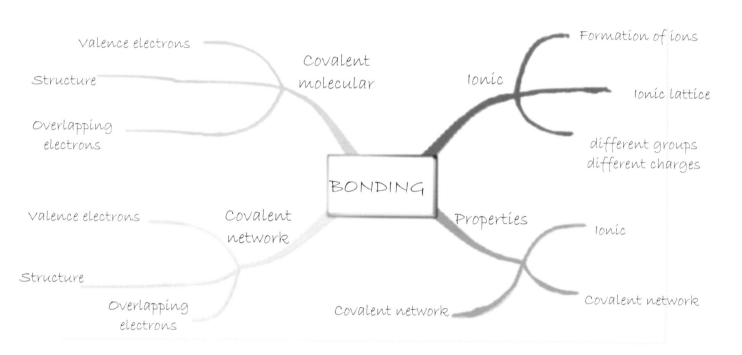

10 Things to do to make great mind maps/spider diagrams

1. Choose just one topic area at a time.
2. Try to jot down as many ideas related to your topic as you can remember.
3. Use your notes to break the topic down into key areas.
4. Use your notes to breakdown the key areas into smaller chunks of information.
5. Label the lines radiating from your key idea & the lines from the next level.
6. Keep the explanations and notes clear and simple.
7. Use images, diagrams and tables to help keep your explanations visual.
8. Use colour to help separate the key ideas.
9. Try to make it visually exciting to help you remember.
10. Use large sheets of paper so the information is easy to read.

Creating Flash Cards

Flash cards help you learn in two ways. The first way is when you make up the cards. Think up a question related to a particular topic and write that down on one side of the card, then find the correct answer and write that down on the other side. If you make sure this is all your own work, you will really benefit from doing it. It is absolutely fine to use your notes or this book to help, that way you'll know you are asking a valid question and writing down the right answer.

The second way is when you use the cards to test yourself, as this is a really quick way of testing whether or not you know something. You can just test yourself or get a group of your class mates to test each other or even members of your family.

There are lots of websites that make creating flash cards easy. Try some of the following:

http://www.cram.com/flashcards/create

http://www.kitzkikz.com/flashcards/

http://www.freetech4teachers.com/2009/07/10-places-to-make-and-find-flashcards.html

10 Things to do to make great flash cards

1. Choose just one topic area at a time
2. Use pictures and images to make your flash cards more memorable.
3. Choose whether you want your flash cards to test you or help you remember information and ideas.
4. For tests keep the questions precise so that your answers can be short and to the point.
5. For cards to help you remember try to have key phrases that are short and easy to remember.
6. Keep the explanations and notes clear and simple.
7. Use images, diagrams and tables to help keep your explanations visual.
8. Use colour to help emphasise key points.
9. Have more than one card giving the same information but in a slightly different way.
10. Shuffle your flash cards so that the order you look at them changes.

An example is given for revising Atoms and the Periodic Table.

The noble gases are found in	Over 100
The transition metals are found in the	groups
Describe alkali metals	periods
Describe Noble Gases	they only contain 1 type of atom
Names the two liquid elements at room temperature	Group 1
Describe the inside of the atom	Group 7

How many elements are listed on the Periodic table?	Group 0
Vertical columns of elements are called	middle of the main groups
Horizontal rows of elements are called	Very reactive metals
Elements are simple because	Very unreactive non-metals
The alkali metals are found in	bromine and mercury
The halogens are found in	a tiny nucleus containing protons and neutrons surrounded by electrons